oat Dock

NORTH
WING

HOUSE

SOUTH
WING

Farm

Landing
Strip

Apple
Orchard

LABORATORIES

CLIFF

D1208633

SPINDRIFT ISLAND

THE CAVES OF FEAR

The RICK BRANT SCIENCE-ADVENTURE *Stories*

BY JOHN BLAINE

———•———

At the sound of the first knuckle, a portion of the roof had risen forming.

At the base of the Black Buddha, a section of the floor
had swung upward.

The Caves of Fear

136

A RICK BRANT SCIENCE-ADVENTURE STORY

THE CAVES OF FEAR

BY JOHN BLAINE

GROSSET & DUNLAP PUBLISHERS

NEW YORK, N. Y.

Printed in the United States of America

Contents

Contents

THE CAVES OF FEAR

CHAPTER I

Changes at Spindrift

THE SOUNDS of hammer and saw had disturbed Spindrift Island for several days, and Rick Brant was having a hard time getting used to it. The noise didn't bother him. It was the idea behind the noise—the idea that the close fellowship of the famous island was about to be intruded upon by strangers.

He sat in a comfortable chair on the front porch of the big Brant house and stared morosely at the Atlantic. He was a tall, athletic boy with brown hair and eyes and a face that was usually pleasant.

"What's it going to be like with a mob of strangers galloping all over the place?" he demanded.

Don Scott grinned lazily from the depths of his armchair. He was a husky youth, perhaps an inch taller than Rick, with black hair and dark eyes. "Since when do five people make a mob?" he inquired. "Besides, I think adding more scientists to the staff is a good thing. So does Dad."

"I know it," Rick returned gloomily. "The others do, too. I'm a downtrodden minority. No one sympathizes with me."

Scotty shook his head sadly. "Poor old Rick. Seriously, I don't get it. You should be cheering the loudest. Think of what it means, pal! More fields of science to explore, including one I never heard of before. Maybe more expeditions, of different kinds than the ones we've been on up to now."

"That's what I'm thinking about," Rick returned.

"Then why the gloom?"

"Because . . ." Rick stopped as the phone rang in the house.

Scotty got to his feet quickly. "I'll get it. Mom and Dad are down watching the builders."

Rick smiled as Scotty went into the house. It pleased him to have Scotty call Mr. and Mrs. Brant "Mom and Dad." It was a symbol of Scotty's permanence in the family. No one had ever questioned Scotty's membership in the Spindrift tribe since the day when the scrappy ex-Marine had rescued Rick from a gang of thugs bent on destroying the Island Foundation's moon rocket, and it was pleasant to think of Scotty as a permanent brother. The two of them had been through some tight places together and they were closer friends than brothers usually are. Like Rick, Scotty was listed on the membership rolls of the Spindrift Foundation as a junior technician.

Hartson W. Brant was listed as president, but it was Rick's pride that he and Scotty had earned places because of their own worth, and not because of their relationship with the scientist. However, their abilities were not the same. Because of Rick's interest in science, particularly electronics, he had become expert in intricate wiring and he was rapidly learning about the design of equipment. Scotty's talent was in the mechanical field. He could repair machinery and he was a whiz with engines.

Thinking about work in the lab reminded Rick that he had an unfinished project of his own on his workbench upstairs. He was half out of his chair, determined to go upstairs and put the rest of the afternoon to good use, when Scotty called.

"Rick! Hurry up."

He ran into the library and found Scotty holding the phone. "Here's a funny one, Rick. The Whiteside telegraph office has a cable for you, but they won't read it over the phone because it's all numbers. And it's from Chahda."

Chahda, the Hindu boy who had been like a member of the family since he joined a Spindrift expedition in Bombay, was back home in India. He had left the boys in New Caledonia after a recent adventure in order to visit his family.

"I'd better talk to them," Rick said. "Who's on the wire?"

"Bill Martin."

Rick took the phone. "Bill? This is Rick. What's up?"

"Got a cable addressed to you," Bill answered. "I'd rather not try to read it over the phone because it's all numbers. Can you or Scotty pick it up?"

"Where's it from?" Rick asked.

"Singapore. And it's signed by your Indian friend."

Singapore! What on earth was Chahda doing in Singapore? Rick couldn't guess. "Bill, what kind of numbers are they?"

"Groups. Seven figures in each group. If you ask me, it's some kind of code."

Rick thought quickly. "Barby's in Whiteside, Bill. She went over to a movie right after lunch, and she should just about be getting out. You can get her next door at the Sugar Shop, because she always stops in there for a fudge sundae after the show. If she's already gone, phone the boat landing. You ought to catch her one place or the other."

"I'll try," Bill promised. "If I don't catch her, I'll call you back."

"Thanks a million." Rick restored the phone to its cradle and looked at Scotty. "What do you make of that?"

Scotty shrugged. "It beats me. I didn't know Chahda was planning to leave Bombay. If it comes to that, I didn't know he knew anything about codes."

"Neither did I," Rick agreed. "Remember he said something about a job in his last letter? There was something secret about it he couldn't tell us. Maybe that's why he's in Singapore."

"Could be. Anyway, we won't know for sure until we get the cable and decipher it. If we *can* decipher it, that is."

"We'll be able to," Rick said confidently. "He wouldn't send us one we couldn't break."

Scotty nodded. "I hope you're right. Well, let's go back and get lazy again."

"Not me." Rick started for the stairs. "I'm going to stop loafing and get busy. The lenses for the camera arrived a week ago and I haven't even looked at them."

"I'll go with you. I got some questions about these new people maybe you can answer."

Upstairs in Rick's bedroom, Scotty sat down in the old leather armchair while Rick opened up the doors that concealed his workbench. On the bench was a camera with an odd-looking searchlight and telescope attached. The searchlight gave off invisible infrared rays instead of ordinary light, and the telescope was equipped with special lenses in order to pick up the infrared. When the camera was loaded with special film, it could take pictures in total darkness, provided the subject was within range of the infrared light rays.

The camera had played a major part in solving the mystery of *Smugglers' Reef*. With the evidence collected from Rick's pictures, the police had broken up a ring of gunrunners. But Rick still was not satisfied with the camera. He was always striving to find the simplest way of doing a thing.

This time, he was planning to eliminate both the spring-driven dynamo that powered the searchlight, and the infrared telescope. A new-type battery in a small metal case already had been mounted under the camera, far enough to one side so it wouldn't interfere with the tripod mount. The battery would give ten hours of service, and it could be replaced in a moment with a spare carried in the pocket.

To take the place of the telescope, Rick had ordered lenses made of the special glass that could "see" infrared. He intended to put the lenses in ordinary sunglasses frames, restore the regular view finder to the camera, and turn the telescope over to Scotty. By using the eyeglasses with special lenses he could see whatever the infrared searchlight was lighting up without the need of looking through the special telescope. Using the glasses and searchlight on the camera together, he could see perfectly in the darkness, and he could take movies, too, if he wanted to.

He went to work removing the telescope.

"I've checked," Scotty said. "That 'scope will fit the mount on my rifle with no changes."

Scotty already had a telescopic sight on his rifle, and the telescope from the infrared unit could be put in its place with a simple turn of a screw. The infrared 'scope and light originally had been designed for a rifle to be used by soldiers at night. Rick had simply adapted the unit to his own needs.

"We can get in some night skunk hunting," Scotty said. "You put the infrared on 'em and take their pictures and I'll sight in through the special 'scope and shoot 'em."

Rick slipped the telescope out of its mount and handed it to Scotty. "If there's one thing I don't need," he said, "it's a dead skunk. Couldn't we hunt prairie moose instead?"

"What's a prairie moose?" Scotty demanded.

"A field mouse with horns."

Scotty groaned. "All right, scientist. Let's get serious and see if you can answer this one. We have an archeologist, a naturalist, and a cyberneticist coming. I think I know what the first two are, but what in the name of a blue baboon is a cyberneticist?"

Rick put the camera view finder into place and began to adjust it. "A specialist in cybernetics," he said.

Scotty waved his arms. "Now I know!" he exclaimed triumphantly. "Any idiot knows what cybernetics is. Or what they are. Ten cents apiece at any hardware counter. No family should be without a handy-dandy cybernetic!"

Rick chuckled. "All right. Cybernetics is a combined study of machines and the human nervous system. It's trying to figure out how machines and humans are related. I don't know much about it myself, but I do know this: the big electronic calculators that do problems in a few hours that it would take humans hundreds of years to finish were the result of cybernetics."

"The big brains!" Scotty looked awed. "I've read about them. And to think we're going to have that kind of expert here!"

"With his wife and two kids," Rick added. "I wonder how Huggins will like a crowd of kids trampling through his garden!"

Scotty laughed outright. "Here we go again! Listen, Rick, start making sense. How can twins less than a year old trample anyone's garden?"

Rick didn't try to answer. He finished the adjustment on the camera and put it back on the shelf, then started to work replacing the lenses in an old pair of sunglasses with the special ones he had ordered. After a moment, he asked, "Scotty, how would you like it if an expedition left Spindrift and we weren't with it?"

Scotty stared. "My sainted aunt! Is that's what's been bothering you?"

Rick admitted it. He knew where he stood with the old gang, Hartson Brant, Hobart Zircon, Julius Weiss, and John Gordon. He was far from sure of how the new staff members would look on him and Scotty. He had learned that some scientists had little patience with people who were unfamiliar with their special fields, and he and Scotty were pretty ignorant about the new sciences that would be represented. That was his only reason for objecting when his father had decided to enlarge the staff.

"I can see it now," he said. "The Foundation will be planning an expedition, maybe to be headed by this new naturalist, and we'll be on the outside looking in. And why? Because Dr. Howard Shannon prefers not to be bothered by a couple of kids who wouldn't know one bug from another."

"You're crossing bridges before you come to 'em," Scotty pointed out. "For all you know, all three of these new scientists might be perfectly swell gents, like Zircon, Weiss, and Gordon. Why borrow trouble in advance?"

"I suppose you're right," Rick had to agree. "But I still can't help thinking about it."

"Think all you like," Scotty said generously. "Me, I'm going to put my little gray brain cells to work on Chahda's cable. Aren't you all fired up with curiosity?"

Rick started to say he was, but no reply was necessary because just then he heard the sound of the motorboat engine for which his ears had been attuned. He put down the sunglasses and ran for the door. Scotty had heard the engine, too, and was halfway down the hall.

It had to be Barby, Rick was sure. The other motorboat—the island had two—was tied up at the pier, and they weren't expecting any visitors. The builders had their own boat, a powered barge, anchored off Pirate's Field.

The boys ran out on the front porch and around the house, then down the long flight of stairs that led to the cove where the motorboat landing was located.

It was Barby, sure enough, and she had the cable! She waved it wildly, then gunned the boat around neatly so that it slid into the dock. Scotty grabbed the bow line and made fast while Rick jumped for the stern line and slipped it around a cleat on the landing.

Barby cut the engine and jumped to the dock, a slim, pretty girl, her face flushed with excitement. "It's from Chahda," she said breathlessly, "and it's in code!"

"We know," Scotty said. "Here, let's take a look at it."

Barby handed it to him. He scanned it wordlessly, then handed it to Rick. "Son, we'll be doing right well if we make any sense out of that!"

"He wouldn't send us anything in a code we couldn't read," Rick objected. "Let's see it. It can't be too hard."

But in the next moment he changed his mind. His lips pursed in a low whistle. This was the cable:

RICK BRANT
SPINDRIFT ISLAND
NEW JERSEY, U.S.A.

5213039	6231581	1219456	2768612	2144644	9123299
3970731	6017747	1044914	3327116	6074193	4399693
0531612	1330552	3047171	3193986	8128912	7011716
0762878	3377335	3831075	5371011	3552684	3012963
3532456	8337373	9104476	1605588	2540551	2826677
9513148	3189710	4811223	5202998	5912492	3432174
3302710	7072010	1510108	4423007	3331954	7893623

L. CHAHDA

CHAPTER II

The Cipher Message

BARBY, Rick, and Scotty were in the library when Hartson Brant walked in. They were reduced to the point of staring at each other helplessly because of the magnitude of the task that confronted them.

The famous scientist, who looked like an older version of his son, greeted them with a smile. "What is this, a meeting of the Silent Three? I can't ever remember finding you all together when one of you wasn't talking."

Rick handed him the cable. "What do you make of that, Dad?"

Hartson Brant scanned it quickly. "From Chahda, in Singapore, and in cipher. Am I supposed to gather that you don't have the key to the cipher?"

"That's right," Scotty said. He held up a heavy volume called *Cryptography for the Student*. It was the only book on the subject in the scientist's library. "We've been going through this, trying to find some kind of clue. Honest, it's impossible."

"There are so many codes and ciphers," Barby added. "Dozens. And it says some of them can only be broken by days of work, by experts."

"There's not an expert in the house, either," Rick concluded. "I didn't think, when Bill called us up about it, that Chahda would use a code we couldn't figure out, but I didn't expect a page like that."

Hartson Brant read through the cable again. "How do you know you can't figure it out? Perhaps a little reasoning will clear the air. Chahda must have put a key in the message somewhere. How about this 'L' in front of his name?"

"That's right," Barby said excitedly. "That must mean something, because his name is Chahda Sundararaman. There isn't an L in it anywhere."

The scientist handed the cable back to Rick. "I'm about as curious as I can get," he said, "but I refuse to think any more about it until you hand me the clear version. I agree that Chahda wouldn't send a code you couldn't solve, so my advice is put the code book away. You won't need it, I'm sure. This isn't any code you'll find in there."

He started out of the room, then paused at the door, his eyes twinkling. "Will you have dinner at the table with us, or shall I ask mother to break out some emergency rations so you can stay on the job?"

"We'll eat with the family," Scotty replied. "We can keep on thinking while we eat, can't we?"

Rick watched his father wink at Barby, then walk toward the kitchen. "Dad's right," he announced. "He must be. So let's put the book back and start figuring this out. The answer probably is easy as pie once we find the key."

"How about starting with that odd letter?" Scotty asked. "That has to mean something."

"L is the twelfth letter in the alphabet," Barby offered. "Does that mean anything?"

Rick shook his head. "Not to me. But let's start from there, anyway. Maybe the twelfth group of numbers has a clue."

He counted rapidly across the number groups. "That group is 4399693. Now what?"

Scotty suggested, "Substitute letters for the numbers. That would make it DCIIFIC. That doesn't mean anything."

"Maybe you counted the wrong way," Barby said thoughtfully. "Count down the columns instead of across."

Rick did so. "That's 8337373. Substitute and it comes out . . . let's see . . . HCCGCGC. Nothing there, either."

Scotty had a pad of paper and a pencil and was making idle doodles. "I'm trying to recall. When did Chahda learn anything about codes?"

Rick thought for a moment. "He never did, that I know of," he said finally.

Barby stood up. "Well, I'm going to shower and change before dinner," she announced. "But I'll keep thinking. I have an idea that talking about it won't help much. If Dad and Rick are right about his using a code we're sure to know, it must be staring us in the face and we're too blind to see it."

"Good idea," Rick agreed. "Let's break this up and each think about it. If we each search our memories, maybe we'll come up with a clue."

Barby went upstairs and Scotty retired to his favorite seat on the porch. But Rick felt that he could think better on his feet. A glance at his watch told him he had over an hour and a half before dinner. He waved at Scotty and walked across the grass toward the gray stone laboratory buildings. Professor Weiss was in his office working on some mathematical theory he was developing. It was away over Rick's head. For a moment he thought of posing the problem to the little professor, then thought better of it and passed by the lab on the south side. He skirted the woods and crossed Pirate's Field, so called because local legend said the famed woman pirate, Anne Bonney, had once landed there with her gang of cutthroats. He paused for a moment and studied the fused sand left by the terrific heat when the first moon rocket was launched, but the barren patch gave him no inspiration.

Staying on the shore path, he walked slowly toward the back of the island and presently came out at the tidal flats. The tide was out, leaving the rocks exposed. He sat down at the edge of the low bluff above the flats and stared into the patches of water.

It was a hard job, trying to recall every detail of his

friendship with the little Hindu boy, but he tried. It had started in Bombay when Rick and Scotty were on their way to Tibet with Weiss and Zircon to set up the radar relay station for message transmission via the moon. When their equipment was stolen, it was Chahda who took the lead in finding it again. They had been amused by the beggar boy who had educated himself with an old copy of *The World Almanac*. His ability to quote anything from the "Alm-in-ack," as he called it, in English that was sometimes pretty funny, was really astonishing. Then, at the Lost City, he had more than proved his courage and loyalty, and the Spindrifters had sponsored his visit to America as a reward.

For a while Chahda had attended school in America, then he had gone to the Pacific with the Spindrift expedition to Kwangara Island. After salvaging the remains of an ancient temple from one hundred fathoms of water—not to mention the treasure that was found—the Spindrifters had returned home. But Chahda had elected to remain in Hawaii with Professor Warren of the Pacific Ethnographic Society. Later, he had gone with the Warren scientific expedition to the South Seas, and Barby, Rick, and Scotty had joined the party in New Caledonia. After completing part of the expedition's work, the trawler *Tarpon* had returned to New Caledonia where the young people had solved the mystery of *The Phantom Shark*. When the three Spindrifters returned home, Chahda had taken air passage to Bombay to see his family.

"I can't remember all we talked about," Rick muttered to himself. "We talked about everything and anything. Except codes. I can't remember that we ever talked about codes."

He got up, noticing that the crew of builders were in their barge, returning to the mainland for the night. They were trucking materials to a point on the shore near Spindrift, using an old wood road, then taking the stuff the rest of the way by barge.

It was getting on to dinnertime. He took the woods path back, passing by the new cottages. They were nearing completion, the outsides already finished. Beyond the cottages was the farm run by the Huggins family. Mr. Huggins was just herding the island's milk cows into the barn for milking.

Rick kicked at a near-by tree. "Either I'm dumb or it isn't as simple as we think it ought to be," he said aloud, then went on into the house.

Scotty and Barby had done no better. They gathered at the family table with long faces and Barby placed the disturbing cable in the middle of the table as a centerpiece.

"If we look at it long enough, maybe we'll get inspiration," she said.

Professor Julius Weiss, the only one of the three staff scientists who was at home at the moment, picked up the cable and examined it.

"A cipher, eh?" He adjusted his glasses. "It certainly looks complicated."

"Any ideas?" Rick asked hopefully.

The little mathematician shook his head. "No, Rick. I could give you the cube root of the square of the sum of the numbers, or anything like that, but I'm afraid I wouldn't even know how to start breaking the code." He added, "John probably could. He had some experience with codes while in the Navy, I believe."

John was Professor John Gordon. He was on an extended trip to New Mexico, serving as a consultant to the Navy's guided missiles projects. The third scientist, Professor Hobart Zircon, was giving a five-week series of lectures in nuclear physics at Yale.

"I'm afraid Professor Gordon is too far away to help us on this," Rick said.

Mrs. Brant came in, bringing a heavily laden dish of fresh corn on the cob. Behind her trotted a shaggy little dog.

Rick snapped his fingers. "Here, Diz."

Dismal ran over and barked at his young master, then he rolled over on his back and played dead, his only trick. Rick grinned. "Did you bring him along as an adviser, Mom? I'll bet he'd be as good at solving this as any of us."

Mrs. Brant smiled. "From what your father told me, I think he might at that. But why all the long faces? I think it's exciting getting a code message from Chahda. Why, this is the first time we've had a code problem on the island since the moon rocket."

Mrs. Brant couldn't have caused a more sudden reaction had she tossed a lighted firecracker into the middle of the roast.

Barby knocked over her water glass.

Scotty gasped, "Great grasshoppers! A book code!"

Rick strangled on a sip of milk, and when he could get his breath again, he ran around the table to his mother, kissed her soundly and lifted her hand high in token of victory. "The new champ," he proclaimed. "Mom, you're a genius!"

"But, Rick, I didn't say anything except . . ."

"You said just enough, dear," Hartson Brant replied. "We all had the answer right in that second, because you gave us a clue. Do you remember the code our former friend used when he was sending messages off the island?"

The "former friend" Hartson Brant referred to was a member of the staff who had turned renegade and helped Manfred Wessel's gang in their efforts to build a moon rocket, using the Spindrift design, in order to win the Stoneridge Grant of two million dollars. The traitor scientist had used code messages to keep the gang informed of new developments on Spindrift while he had used the cloak of false friendship to slow up the building of the Spindrift rocket.

"He used a double code," Rick explained. "Part of it was a regular cipher, but the first step was a book code."

"I do remember!" Mrs. Brant exclaimed. "He used a copy of that book Hartson's friend wrote. What was it? *Psychiatry Simplified.* The code was numbers that gave the page of the book, and the position of the word on the page, and unless you found the book, as Rick and Scotty did, you couldn't break the code!"

Barby jumped up in her excitement. "And I know what book Chahda was using!"

The rest of the group spoke as one. "*The World Almanac!*"

Scotty ran for the library, Rick on his heels.

"We told him about that code," Scotty said. "Now I remember when, too. It was right after we got back from India, when we were showing him around the lab."

"I remember, too," Rick agreed. "We were telling him how the gang used my plane, with me flying it, to smuggle their coded messages, and he asked us about it because he had never heard of codes before!"

They reached the shelf that held the *Almanac* and stopped short. Because of the year-to-year news summaries in the famous annual, Hartson Brant had kept each edition as a reference source. There were over a dozen of them on the shelf.

"They're all different," Rick said. "The pages change each year. Which one did he use?"

Scotty's forehead furrowed. "Which one did he memorize? It was an old one, but I can't remember the date."

"Got it," Rick said. "Remember the letter L? The twelfth letter of the alphabet. It must be the 1912 edition."

Scotty surveyed the shelf. "Which we don't have," he said.

Rick groaned. "No!"

Hartson Brant called from the dining room. "Haven't you solved that cipher yet?"

The boys walked dejectedly back to join the others. Rick explained that the right volume was missing. The Spindrift files just didn't go back that far.

"Sit down and eat your dinner," Hartson Brant said. He sliced roast for them, his eyes thoughtful. "Something's wrong with your reasoning," he said, as he filled Rick's plate. "Would Chahda have a 1912 edition with him in Singapore? I doubt it. More likely he'd have a more recent one."

"But the letter L has to mean something," Barby protested.

"What could it mean but twelve?" Rick asked, and the answer struck him before the words were out. He shouted, "I know! It could mean fifty! L is the Roman numeral fifty."

Barby clapped her hands. Scotty reached over and pounded Rick on the back.

"That's it," Hartson Brant said approvingly. "I'll make a wager on it. Chahda used the 1950 edition."

Rick pushed back his chair, but the scientist's voice stopped him.

"Let's rest on our laurels, Rick. Finish dinner first, then we'll all retire to the library and work it out."

Because they were burning with impatience, the three younger members of the Spindrift family did not enjoy the meal, but they made a pretense of eating. Then, an eternity later, Hartson Brant took the last sip of his coffee and grinned at Rick. "Shall we get to it?"

"Shall we!" Barby led the way, holding the cable high.

The first part was easy. Since most pages in the *Al-*

manac had three numbers, they assumed that the first three numbers in each code group referred to the page. Similarly, they assumed that the second two numbers referred to the line. That left two numbers for the position of the word on the line.

With nervous fingers Rick turned to Page 521 of the 1950 edition and counted down 30 lines. He hesitated over the subtitles, then decided to count them too. At the proper line, he looked up at Scotty and Barby who were watching over his shoulder.

"But there are two columns."

"Don't worry about the columns," Scotty advised. "I don't think Chahda would pay any attention to the columns, because it would mean extra numbers in each group. Count right across and don't pay any attention to the dividing line."

Rick did so. "It doesn't come out right," he complained. "The number is 39, but there are only 17 words on the whole line."

Barby sighed. "Maybe we're wrong all the way around."

"I don't think so," Hartson Brant said. He was sitting in a comfortable chair, smoking an after-dinner pipe. "The logic of the thing appeals to me. Do you suppose Chahda would know about nulls?"

"What's a null?" Scotty asked.

"In cryptography it's a number, or letter, thrown in for the sake of appearance, or to confuse."

"Chahda might know," Rick said. "That brown head of his is crammed full of more odd chunks of information than you could imagine. But if there's a null in this, which figure is it?"

"Try it both ways," Barby urged. "Here, I'll do it." She counted across the line. "The third word is 'seventeen.'" She wrote it down. "The ninth word is 'come.'"

"Could be either," Scotty mused. "But 'come' sounds more likely. Let's try the next group."

That was 6231581. Rick turned to Page 623 and counted down 15 lines, including the title. However, he didn't count the page heading. The heading was on the same line as the page number. Both were above a line drawn across the top of the page, and it seemed sensible to start below the line.

"There aren't 81 words on the lines," he said. "So that means another null, maybe. The first word is 'both' and the eighth word is 'may.'"

Barby wrote them down. "It all makes sense," she pointed out. "It could be, 'Seventeen may,' or 'come both.'"

"Keep going," Scotty urged. "Try another one."

The third group gave them a choice of "Cheyenne," which seemed unlikely, or "bad."

"He couldn't be talking about Cheyenne," Rick said. "The word must be 'bad.' That means the first figure of the pair is the null, because it's the second figure that stands for 'bad.'"

"Sounds reasonable," Scotty agreed. "Keep plugging."

So far, the probable words were: *Come both bad.*

Page 276 in the fourth group turned out to be a table of atomic weights. Line 86 was the element tantalum.

If the first figure of the last pair was assumed to be a null, the word was the symbol for tantalum: "Ta."

Rick stared at it. "Something's wrong. This doesn't make sense."

Barby asked impatiently, "How do we know?"

Rick yielded and moved to the next group. It gave the word "rubles." "That's Russian money," he said.

The trio looked at it in bewilderment, then Scotty suddenly let out a yell of laughter. "I've got it! Can't you see? 'Ta' and 'rubles' go together! 'Tarubles.' Troubles!"

Then they were all howling with joy. Leave it to Chahda to dream up something like that, Rick thought. So far, the message made sense. *Come both, bad troubles.*

He turned the pages and counted feverishly. The sixth group gave "am," the seventh "in."

The eighth group gave the message an ominous tone. *Come both. Bad troubles. Am in danger.*

The scientists and Mrs. Brant were looking over Rick's shoulder now, too.

The ninth group stopped them for a moment because the pair of figures standing for the word was 14. If the figure 1 was a null, the word was "the." But there were more than 14 words in the line, and the 14th was "my."

Rick looked at the faces around him. "I think it's 'my' because he must have had a reason for using nulls. If I were making up the code, I'd use them because sometimes there are enough words in a line so you need two figures and sometimes not. But you always have to put down two figures so the groups will be even."

"Good thinking," Rick's father complimented him. "Go ahead on that basis. But hurry up. The suspense is awful."

There was a chorus of agreements.

The next word was "boss."

"He was working, then," Scotty guessed. "That must be it, if he has a boss."

Rick hurried to the next group. It produced "Carl." Page 439, the 96th line, gave "Bradley." Then the boss's name was Carl Bradley.

Hartson Brant gave a muffled exclamation. Scotty turned quickly. "Do you know that name, Dad?"

"Yes. But let's get the rest of the message. Quickly, Rick."

The words appeared in rapid succession, with a pause now and then to solve a new difficulty. Once, the lines across the columns were not even and a ruler had to be laid across to find the word. Again, a null appeared as the first number in the page group. Chahda had used it because the page was 51 and he needed a third figure to round out the group. That was easy to spot because the group read 951 and the book had only 912 pages.

In the last series of groups Rick came across another double word like "tarubles." This time, "be" and "ware" combined to make "beware." Then, the very last word stopped them for a moment. It was "umbra."

"What's that?" Scotty asked.

"The shadow cast by the moon during an eclipse of the sun," Julius Weiss answered. "Or part of it, rather. There are two shadows. The umbra and the penumbra."

Barby ran for a dictionary and leafed through the pages quickly. "I have it," she said. "Listen. It's from the Latin for 'shadow,' and it means 'a shade or shadow.'"

"Shadow it is," Rick said, and wrote it down. Then, slowly, he read the full message to the serious group around him.

COME BOTH. BAD TROUBLES. AM IN DANGER. MY BOSS, CARL BRADLEY, DISAPPEARED. GOVERNMENT WILL ASK SCIENTIFIC FATHER DO SPECIAL WORK. MUST TAKE. GET JOBS, MEET ME HONG KONG GOLDEN MOUSE. WATCH CHINESE WITH GLASS EYE, HE DANGEROUS. AND BEWARE LONG SHADOW.

CHAPTER III

Heavy Water

HARTSON BRANT walked swiftly to the telephone and picked it up.

"What's the matter, Dad?" Rick asked quickly. The scientist had a strange look on his face.

"Give me the telegraph office," Hartson Brant said. He put his hand over the mouthpiece. "I'll tell you in a moment. I want to get a wire off immediately." He spoke into the phone again. "Western Union? This is Spindrift, Brant speaking. I want to send a straight telegram. Yes. To Steven Ames."

Risk gasped. Steve Ames was the young intelligence officer of JANIG, the secret Army-Navy group charged with protecting the security of American government secrets. The Spindrift group of scientists had worked with Steve in solving *The Whispering Box Mystery*.

Scotty's fingers bit into Rick's arm.

Hartson Brant gave the address. "Here's the message. 'Have reconsidered your request basis of new information just received here. Urge you come or phone at once.' That's it. Sign it 'Brant, Spindrift.' Yes. Charge to this number."

He waited until the telegraph office had read back the message, then hung up and turned to the waiting group.

"Three days ago I had a phone call from Steve Ames. He asked if I could undertake a special job for the government that would require me to go overseas at once for an indefinite time. I was forced to decline because obviously I can't leave now with these staff changes about to take place."

The scientist knocked the ashes out of his pipe, his face thoughtful.

"Steve wouldn't take no for an answer. He insisted that the job was of the utmost importance, and he added that it concerned an old college chum of mine." He paused. "His name is Carl Bradley."

Rick's eyes met Scotty's.

"He said it was an urgent job, but that he would give me a few days to think it over, to see if I couldn't rearrange my affairs in some way. I assured him it was no use, that I couldn't possibly leave, but he said to take until Saturday to consider it. That's tomorrow."

Rick whistled. "Some timing."

"It's a lot more than mere coincidence," Hartson Brant said. "But I don't know any more about it than what I've told you."

"Who is Carl Bradley?" Weiss asked.

"I'm surprised you haven't heard of him, Julius. He

has a considerable reputation as an ethnologist. He and Paul Warren and I were in school together. We lost track of him for a while, then he wrote from China. He had spent several years inland, living with the Chinese, as one of them. He produced some immensely valuable studies. Those, and his rather remarkable ability to speak and act like a Chinese earned him the nickname of 'Chinese Bradley.' He had lived most of his life since school in one part of Asia or another. But I'm sure I can't guess what his connection is with this special job of Steve's, or how he happened to become Chahda's boss."

"Or why he's missing," Barby added.

The cable had created a mystery that demanded a solution, but not amount of discussion answered the questions it raised. Finally, Mrs. Brant broke up the debate by pointedly remarking on the lateness of the hour. Reluctantly, the family started for bed.

As Rick undressed, he continued the discussion through the door connecting his room and Scotty's. "Chahda's pretty sure we'll hurry to Hong Kong."

"Is he wrong?" Scotty demanded.

"I don't know," Rick said. "It depends on a lot of things. We can't go unless we get jobs, and Steve evidently didn't say anything to Dad about the rest of the staff, including us."

"Dad hasn't even said he'll go," Scotty reminded.

"Doesn't saying he has reconsidered mean that he'll go?"

"Could be. Or maybe it just means he's willing to talk

some more about it. We should have pinned him down."

"We will," Rick said. "In the morning."

He lay awake for long hours, staring into the darkness and trying to piece together Chahda's references to a golden mouse, a Chinese with a glass eye, and a long shadow. It was no use. But there was no mistaking the urgency of his friend's plea.

Where was Chahda now? At a guess, somewhere between Singapore and Hong Kong. But whether by land or sea or air, Rick couldn't imagine. Nor could he even venture a wild guess at what kind of danger Chahda faced.

After a long time he fell asleep, but it was fitful sleep broken by frequent awakenings.

In the morning, the discussion resumed over breakfast, bringing forth wild speculations from Barby. Rick had to grin at her flights of fancy.

"One thing seems sure," Scotty offered. "Chahda was in a big hurry."

"What makes you think so?" Mrs. Brant asked. "Barby! Please stop feeding Dismal at the table."

Dismal turned beseeching eyes to Rick in a plea for moral support, but his young master was listening to Scotty.

"The words he used. Like putting together an atomic symbol and Russian money to make 'troubles,' and using 'umbra' instead of shadow. I'm sure in a big book like The World Almanac troubles and shadows are mentioned somewhere. But he didn't have time to search. He took the first possibilities that came along."

Rick nodded approval. "That figures. But why didn't he have time?"

Scotty shrugged. "Your guess is as good as mine. Maybe better."

Julius Weiss, who had tired of the discussion and started to the lab, ran back into the house. "There's a plane heading this way," he announced. "I'm sure it's coming here, because it's down pretty low."

The conversation ended abruptly. Rick and Scotty were first out on the lawn. The engine noise of the plane was loud.

Rick saw it first, a sleek, four-place cabin job, circling wide out over the water, losing altitude. In a few moments it banked sharply behind the lab building, straightened out, and cut the gun. Rick was running toward the end of the grass strip even before the plane settled smoothly to the ground.

"Steve Ames," he said to himself. "I'll bet it is." The JANIG officer had wasted no time!

Sure enough, Steve was the first out of the plane. Rick saw that he was the only passenger. The pilot got out then, and Rick recognized him as one of the JANIG operatives who had chased the Whispering Box gang across Washington.

Steve and Rick shook hands, grinning at each other, then Rick greeted Mike, the pilot.

"Didn't think we'd be needing Spindrift again so soon," Steve said. He walked to meet the others and shook hands all around. "Let's get busy," he said to Hartson Brant.

Rick, Scotty, and Barby followed the two into the library. Mrs. Brant took the pilot into the dining room for coffee while Professor Weiss excused himself and went on to the laboratory. His apparent lack of interest would have amazed anyone who didn't know him, but Rick knew that when Julius Weiss was wrapped up in one of his theoretical math problems, nothing else on earth could find room in his mind.

Steve looked at the scientist. "What caused you to reconsider?"

"This." Hartson Brant handed him the translation of Chahda's cable, then the original. "We broke the code last night. It was a book code, using *The World Almanac*. Chahda knew we'd be able to puzzle it out."

Steve scanned the number groups briefly. "Clever," he commented. He read through the clear copy twice, and his jaw tightened. "This explains something that has puzzled me."

"A good thing," Rick said. "Because all we got was the puzzlement. No explanations."

Steve tapped the cable thoughtfully. "I hate to ask you to tackle this job, but you must have some ideas about it or you wouldn't have sent that wire."

Hartson Brant nodded. "I explained my situation to you on the phone when you called a few days ago. The situation hasn't changed, but I must admit this cable from Chahda puts a new light on the matter. That boy is a member of the family."

"Then you'll go?"

"I don't want to, quite frankly. I will if there is no

alternative. I lost a lot of sleep last night making that decision. But first, I want to propose that some member of my staff go in my stead."

Steve walked to the desk and perched on its edge. "Which one?"

"You know them all. You also know their specialties. Which of them would fit your requirements best?"

"Zircon. He's a nuclear physicist."

Rick held his breath. Steve was continuing:

"Chahda urges Rick and Scotty to get jobs, too. I hadn't considered that, but it's not a bad idea."

Rick closed his eyes and let out his breath in a sigh of relief. Scotty nudged him.

Hartson Brant asked, "Then you will consider Zircon as my substitute? Always on condition that he will go, of course."

Steve nodded. "I'd prefer you, but I'll take Zircon, if I can make a condition of my own, and that is that you'll fly to the Far East on a moment's notice if he and the boys can't handle it."

Rick looked at his father anxiously. Hartson Brant had not given his permission for them to make a trip, but evidently it was all right. The scientist nodded.

"I'll agree to that." He went to the telephone and picked up the instrument. "Operator, I want to place a long-distance call."

Steve winked at the boys. Then, as Hartson Brant placed the call to Zircon in New Haven, Connecticut, the JANIG man said, "Going to be a couple of tourists at government expense, huh? Pretty soft."

"Maybe," Rick said, grinning. "That cable doesn't sound like anything soft."

Steve got serious. "You two proved yourselves in Washington, so far as I'm concerned. You can make yourselves useful, and you'll provide a good cover for Zircon."

"What kind of cover?" Barby asked.

Steve smiled at her. "Women can't keep secrets, I'm told."

"I can," Barby retorted swiftly.

Steve held up his hand for silence. Hartson Brant had Zircon on the line. The scientist outlined Steve's proposal in a few words, and gave Zircon the contents of Chahda's cable. Then he listened to Zircon while Rick fidgeted anxiously. Finally, Hartson Brant said, "All right, Hobart. Tell your people up there that I'll take your lectures. We'll see you later today." He hung up and nodded at Steve.

"Hobart had lectures scheduled for next week, but I can take them for him. He'll be down this afternoon, and, he says, he'll be ready to leave in the morning if necessary."

"Good!" Steve nodded at Barby. "Even if you can't go on the trip, you can make yourself useful. Want to place a call to Washington for me?"

"Yes," Barby said eagerly. "Where to?"

Steve gave her the number. Then, while she was placing the call, he said, "Now, I'll tell you what I know."

Rick's heart beat faster. Now he would learn what was behind Chahda's cable!

"The day before I phoned here," Steve began, "my office received a message from Carl Bradley. It was a top secret message sent to us via the American consulate general's channels from Singapore. I'd better explain first that Carl is a JANIG man. His knowledge of that part of the world has made him invaluable, and he works for us secretly while doing his routine work as an ethnologist. That is top secret information that must never be repeated outside this room."

"You can depend on us," Hartson Brant assured him.

"I know it. To go on. His job is gathering information about persons who show too much interest in operations within our embassies and consulates. However, the cable we got from him wasn't quite in that line."

Steve paused to see how Barby was getting along. She was trying to listen to him and the operator at the same time.

"This cable," Steve continued, "said he had accidentally made a discovery of something potentially dangerous to America. He asked for a competent nuclear physicist, and he named you, Hartson, to be sent to Singapore at once to check on his finding, and to locate, if possible, the source of the stuff he had discovered. We haven't heard from him since. From Chahda's cable, it's evident something has happened to him. And on the basis of the cable, I think we'll send Zircon and you boys to Hong Kong first."

Scotty put into words the question that was in Rick's mind. "What was it that he discovered?"

Steve's lips tightened, then he said: *"Heavy water!"*

CHAPTER IV

Project X

"HEAVY WATER!" Hartson Brant exclaimed softly

Rick and Scotty looked at each other blankly.

And at that moment, Barby completed the connection and called to Steve. He strode to the phone and picked it up. "Who's this? All right. Steve Ames here. Take down these names. Hobart Zircon. Richard Brant. Donald Scott. You'll find full data on them in the files. Prepare travel orders and get tickets for all three to Hong Kong via the first plane leaving New York after 7:00 P.M. tomorrow night. Arrange for a letter of credit in the usual amount on the National City Bank of Washington, and have the bank make arrangements with all their Far East branches. Put all three on the pay roll at the same grades they held before. Get passports for them with visitor's visas for the Philippines, Hong Kong, Indo-China, Indonesia, Siam, and China. We don't know where they'll end up. Then put all that stuff in an envelope and get it to me here at Spindrift by special

messenger . . . wait, never mind that. I'll send Mike
back right away, and he can bring it to me. Now read
those instructions back."

Steve listened for a moment. "Right. Get going.
What? Oh, charge the whole thing to a new case file.
Mark it Project X."

He disconnected and turned to the group. "Now," he
said grimly, "let's talk turkey."

He nodded at Rick and Scotty. "Zircon said he could
leave in the morning, if necessary. That's rushing you a
little too much. So I've given you until tomorrow night."

Rick grinned. Once things started to move with Steve
Ames, they moved strictly jet-propelled.

"What are we supposed to do?" Scotty asked.

"Find Bradley. If you can. But don't spend too much
time searching. Getting all the dope—and I mean *all*—
on that heavy water is the reason for your going out
there. If you find Bradley, he can help. Maybe Chahda
can help, too. But never forget for a minute that track-
ing down that heavy water is your mission."

"If we don't find Bradley, we won't know how to get
started," Rick pointed out.

Steve grunted. "No? If I believed that, I'd have gone
somewhere else for help. I came here because I knew
Spindrift could give me ingenuity as well as scientific
knowledge. And you hadn't better let me down!"

"We won't let you down," Scotty assured him.

Barby chimed in indignantly, "Of course they won't."

Steve smiled. "Don't worry. I'm not afraid of their
falling down on the job. But it's a big one. I'll tell Zircon

this when he comes, but you can be thinking it over in the meantime. You're to find out who is bringing heavy water to the Asia coast and what they're doing with it. You're to find out where it comes from, and why it is being made. You're to get samples and send them back here. And most important of all, you're to locate and pinpoint for us any industrial plants you find."

Scotty scratched his head. "Fine. Only let's get back to the beginning. What is heavy water? And why are you so excited about it?"

"I don't know, either," Barby added.

Hartson Brant looked at his son. "You do, don't you, Rick?"

"I know what it is, but I don't know why it's so important to Steve," Rick said. He had read a great deal about heavy water in studying elementary physics. It had many uses in physics experiments.

"Let's see how much you know," Steve directed "Sound off."

Rick searched his memory, trying to marshal all the facts he knew. "Well," he began, "ordinary water is composed of oxygen and hydrogen. In every water molecule there are two atoms of hydrogen and one of oxygen. The important part, for what we're talking about, are the hydrogen atoms. Hydrogen is the lightest element, and it has the simplest atom. There's just one proton and one electron."

He looked at his father, waiting for a nod to tell him he was on the right track. When the scientist nodded approval, he went on.

"That kind of hydrogen atom has a mass of one, as the scientists say. But there are other kinds of hydrogen atoms, and they are pretty rare, called isotopes. An isotope is just a different variety of the ordinary kind of atom in each element. The thing that makes it different is a change in the nucleus. Well, hydrogen has two isotopes. One kind, which has a mass of two, is found in nature. It is called deuterium. Its nucleus is called a deuteron. Another kind, which can be made in a nuclear reactor, is called tritium. A little of it is found naturally but not enough to count for much."

He took a deep breath. "I hope I know what I'm talking about."

"You're doing fine," Hartson Brant said. "Go on."

"All right. Well, heavy water is made of one atom of oxygen plus two atoms of deuterium, which is the first isotope of hydrogen. In chemistry, there's no difference in the way heavy water acts. You can even drink it. In fact, people do drink it every day, because in ordinary water there is some heavy water. I forget the exact figures, but I think that, by weight, there are five thousand parts of ordinary hydrogen in water and only one part of deuterium."

"That's right." Steve Ames nodded. "Five thousand to one. Now tell us what is peculiar about all isotopes?"

Rick thought furiously and came up with what he hoped was the answer. "I think it's that isotopes aren't as stable as the basic elements. Some are pretty stable, but some are pretty shaky. That's why some of the isotopes of uranium can be split wide open in a chain reaction to make an atomic bomb, and . . ."

A chill ran through him. His mouth opened. He knew! He knew why heavy water had Steve Ames all excited. He choked:

"Hydrogen bombs!"

Scotty and Barby gasped. Steve Ames and Hartson Brant smiled.

"It's true that one of the possibilities in building a hydrogen bomb concerns deuterium," the scientist said. "But I scarcely think that's the case here. How about it, Steve?"

"Possible, but extremely improbable," Steve agreed. "What I'm most interested in is a use for heavy water Rick hasn't mentioned. Know what a nuclear reactor is, Rick?"

Rick nodded. "It's what the newspapers usually call an 'atomic pile.' We have quite a few in this country, I think. The Atomic Energy Commission said quite a while ago that they used a nuclear reactor with uranium as a fuel to make plutonium, which is the artificial element that can be used in atomic bombs. Besides uranium itself, that is."

"That's right. What I'm interested in is the fact that heavy water can be used as a neutron moderator in a reactor."

Rick looked blank. Steve was talking way over his head. Hartson Brant saw his son's bewilderment and explained: "You've probably heard that the uranium in a reactor is encased in blocks of graphite, which is simply carbon, Rick. It prevents the neutrons from the uranium from simply running wild. Well, heavy water can be used for the same purpose."

"Exactly," Steve said. "So you see, I'm not afraid of the possibility of hydrogen bombs as much as I am of the possibility that somewhere in Asia is a nuclear reactor. Until we get international agreement on atomic weapons, we simply have to keep track of atomic developments everywhere for our own protection. If there's a new country going in for atomic research, and it can build a reactor, it might also be able to build an atomic bomb. Now, don't forget I said heavy water is a legitimate industrial product. We certainly can't object to a nation's manufacturing it. We wouldn't want to. But when it turns up in an odd corner of the world, I think we'd better find out why. If it's a peaceful reason, we'll mark it down and then forget it. If not, we'll make a report to the United Nations."

"Why not report it right now?" Barby asked.

"Good question. The answer is, we're not sure. Remember Carl Bradley was unsure enough to ask for help. If we got up before the UN and started hollering and it turned out to be plain water, we'd look pretty foolish."

"I don't even know how we'd begin," Scotty muttered. "How do you start on a job like this?"

"You'll start by being innocent tourists," Steve said. "You and Rick are students on a holiday, with Zircon, your uncle, as guide and tutor. You'll be interested in a number of things, including hunting. That will give you a good excuse for barging around the country if you have to. But you won't be able to decide what you want to hunt." Steve grinned. "You'll decide after you find out where you have to go. And you'd better learn about Asiatic game animals. For instance, if the trail takes you to Indonesia, you may want to hunt the hairy Sumatran rhinoceros. In the Philippines, you'll hunt timarau, which are a special breed of wild water buffalo. In China, around the coast, you can hunt tigers. In Malaya, if the trail does take you down to Singapore, you can hunt tapir. Same for Siam. In Indo-China you can hunt tigers. Inland in China, toward the Tibetan border, you'd better be hunting bharals."

"That's a wonderful name," Barby said quickly. "What are they?"

"Another name for them is blue sheep," Steve told her. "They're bluish-gray, shading to white in the under parts. The horns are unusual, because they curve outward from the sides of the head, then down and backward."

Hartson Brant paused in the act of filling his pipe and asked curiously, "How do you know so much about Asiatic animals, Steve?"

Steve laughed. "Because I used the same gag once myself." He started for the door. "Talk it over, and think up any questions you can. I won't promise to know the answers, but I'll try. I've got to get Mike started back to Washington to pick up that stuff."

When he had gone, Barby looked enviously at the two

boys. "In my next reincarnation," she announced, "I'm going to be a boy. I don't see why I couldn't go, too. A girl would make the group look even less suspicious, wouldn't it?" She scanned the three faces eagerly, then sighed. "All right. I knew it wasn't any use."

"Never mind, towhead," Rick said. He always hated to see Barby's wistful expression when he and Scotty were going somewhere. "Maybe next time."

"Not if next time is another job like this," Hartson Brant disagreed. He studied his pipe stem, his forehead wrinkled thoughtfully. "I'm not quite sure why I didn't object to Rick and Scotty going."

Rick demanded swiftly, "You're not going to object, are you, Dad?"

"No, Rick. If we hadn't been on other expeditions and in some tough spots together, I surely would. But I know you two are able to take care of yourselves. And so is Zircon. Only keep in mind that you may be dealing with an entirely new breed of cats, unscrupulous men who wouldn't hesitate to put you out of the way without a moment's hesitation. So be careful. Be very careful. Don't take risks that aren't essential to your job. And do what Zircon tells you to without hesitation. He's knocked around in some pretty rough corners of the world, and I don't know a man who is better equipped for this kind of job, unless it's Carl Bradley."

The warning sobered Rick even more. Apart from what his father had said, he knew it was also what the information could mean to the security of the country that had prevented the scientist from making a single objection to their going.

"We'll take no risks we don't have to," he promised. "We'll move as if we were walking on eggs, Dad."

And Scotty echoed the promise.

Nothing remained but to wait for Zircon and make definite plans. Steve, who had risen early in order to get to Spindrift first thing, walked out to the orchard with Dismal for company and stretched out under a tree for a nap.

Rick and Scotty couldn't possibly have napped, so they went up to Rick's room and began to pack. That took little time, since they would travel by air. Scotty took his rifle out of its protective case and cleaned it, then tried on the infrared telescope. He removed from the 'scope the masking bits of cardboard Rick had used to convert it to a camera view finder, thus making it a telescopic rifle sight once more. It fitted perfectly.

"You taking the movie camera along?" he asked.

Rick thought it over. "Guess I will," he said finally. "Tourists are supposed to have cameras. I'll take the movie instead of the speed graphic. And I can take along infrared film as well as regular color film. If anyone asks, I can say I want movies of the animals you and Zircon shoot. Then all three of us won't have to take guns."

"Better finish putting the lenses into those sunglasses frames then," Scotty said.

"I'll do it right now. It won't take long." A thought struck Rick. "What will Zircon do for a rifle?"

"He'll have to borrow one, and an ordinary one won't do, either. If we're supposed to be hunting big game, he'll need one bigger than my .303." Scotty frowned thoughtfully. "How about Captain Douglas? He used to be quite a hunter. You've seen the African trophies in his office at the barracks."

Captain Douglas was commanding officer of the Whiteside State Police Barracks, and a good friend of the boys. He and his officers had co-operated with them in rounding up the Smugglers' Reef gang.

"Give him a phone call while I finish putting these lenses in," Rick suggested.

"Good idea." Scotty went to phone.

More and more Rick was realizing the magnitude of the job they had undertaken. He hoped fervently that Chahda would know something useful in case they failed to locate Bradley.

In a moment Scotty stuck his head in the door. "I've got the captain on the phone," he said. "He's got a .45–90 we can borrow, and, bless his heart, he didn't ask where we were going. When can we pick it up?"

Rick thought it over. "I'll have to fly to the airport and pick up Zircon in a little while. Tell Captain Douglas I'll buzz the barracks on the way over. Ask if he can possibly deliver it to me at the airport. I hate to bother him, but I won't have a car to go get it." Rick's little cub airplane was the island's fast messenger-passenger service.

"Okay." Scotty disappeared down the hall again for a few moments and then returned. He took a seat in the leather armchair. "He finally did get curious. Wanted to know if we needed that caliber rifle to shoot Jersey mosquitoes. I told him we were going on a trip and that I couldn't say anything more about it. So he said he'd lend us the gun only on condition that we tell him the story when we got back. I said we would, if we could."

"He's the best," Rick said. "But he knows we've done some hush-hush work for the government, and don't forget he's an ex-Marine. He wouldn't embarrass us by asking too many questions."

Scotty nodded. "Wait until you see this rifle. A .45–90 is a regular cannon. It'll knock down anything smaller than an elephant, and it'll knock down one of those, if it hits the right spot."

"That's just Zircon's size," Rick said, grinning. The scientist was a huge man who towered over the rest of the staff.

Later, Zircon dominated the library a. Steve issued final instructions. The scientist's booming voice had phrased questions for an hour, until even Steve looked weary.

"This winds up what I have to say," he told them. "Mike should be back with your tickets, passports, and letter of credit in another hour. I'll go back to Washington and issue instructions via the State Department to all of our ambassadors and consuls in the area. They'll know what's happening and why you're there, but no one else on their staffs will. Go in to see each one whose country you enter. Make a lot of noise. Insist on seeing the chief. He'll know your names and he'll do everything he can. Bradley is supposed to check in with each embassy or consulate in the same way. They'll be your points of contact in case he shows up again. File reports when you can. Hand them to the ambassador or consul of the country and no one else."

Steve stopped for a moment, then his warm grin flashed. "This is going to be tougher than beating the Whispering Box gang. I know you'll come back with the answers, but be sure you have whole skins when you do!"

CHAPTER V

Hong Kong

THE FOUR-ENGINE transport had been letting down from its cruising altitude for what seemed like an hour. Rick was watching through the circular window for the first sign of land, and he was getting impatient.

The trip had been a long one. It seemed to Rick that he had been sitting in a plane for most of his life, even though they had been gone from Spindrift for less than four days. That was because they were making no stopovers. At San Francisco, Honolulu, Guam, and Manila they had stopped only long enough to refuel, or to change planes.

Scotty, in the seat next to Rick, was sound asleep. Zircon, across the aisle, was engrossed in a book.

Rick looked up as the stewardess walked past him. She smiled and pointed through the window on the opposite side. He caught a glimpse of mountainous country below. Then, in a few seconds, a small island passed underneath on his own side. They were getting close to the ground now. He estimated their altitude at less than two thousand feet. He poked Scotty in the ribs.

"Rise and shine, mighty hunter. We're getting ready to land."

Scotty was wide awake instantly. "About time," he muttered. "Show me this famous Hong Kong."

"Can't yet," Rick replied. "But we've passed a couple of islands. Look, there's another."

They were dropping rapidly now. The big plane suddenly banked, leveled, then banked again. As they rocked up, Rick looked down into a cove, crowded with Chinese junks. The brief glimpse sent a thrill through him, as new scenes always did. They were the first junks he had seen outside of pictures.

The plane banked again, the other way. Rick realized with a sudden feeling of discomfort that they were actually weaving their way through mountain peaks! He had heard that the approach to Hong Kong was crooked as a corkscrew; now he knew the reports didn't exaggerate.

Zircon was leaning across the aisle. He pointed to a strip of curved beach. "Repulse Bay," he boomed. "We're almost in." The scientist had been to the Far East before, and he knew Hong Kong.

They were close to the top of abrupt hills. Rick saw a road curving through the hills and valleys, then they were over water again, and the water was dotted with modern ships as well as junks. The plane rocked far over in a tight bank, and there was a howl as the flaps were lowered. Rick and Scotty buckled safety belts and sat back as the plane leveled off.

In a few moments they were collecting their luggage and walking across a concrete apron to the customs building. Inside, a Chinese clerk, under the supervision of a British officer, gave their effects a cursory glance, stamped their passports, and handed them police forms to fill out. They did so as rapidly as possible, turned them in, and left the customs room. Outside, they picked up the bags they had checked, gave them to a Chinese coolie, who appeared from nowhere, and followed him to a taxi.

It was a small car of English make. Zircon looked at it with disapproval. "Am I supposed to fit into that thing?" he demanded.

Rick hid a grin. The car wasn't much bigger than the scientist. Zircon squeezed in gingerly, Scotty behind him. Rick got into the front seat with the driver.

"Peninsular Hotel," Zircon directed.

"Funny," Scotty said. "I never expected to find an airport on Hong Kong. All the pictures I've seen of it show mountains. It doesn't look as though there were room for an airport."

"There isn't," Zircon said. "We're not on Hong Kong. This is Kowloon. It's a peninsula jutting out from the mainland of China. However, it's a part of the British Crown Colony of Hong Kong. We'll get to the island itself, and to Victoria, which is the main city, by ferryboat or walla-walla."

"What's that?" Rick asked curiously.

"Local name for a water taxi," Zircon explained.

The taxi was leaving the airport now, but there was nothing in sight at the moment to show that this was the Orient. The modern buildings were of stone, brick, and concrete, and the streets were wide and clean. As they got closer to downtown Kowloon, however, Chinese predominated, with only a sprinkling of what were evidently Englishmen. In a short time they pulled up in front of the Peninsular, one of the world's famous hotels. It was an imposing structure, the lobby as vast as an auditorium but broken up by numerous pillars, potted plants, and dusty-looking furniture. They registered and were shown to a very large and comfortable room with a window that opened on a fire escape.

As Zircon tipped the Chinese bearers, Rick asked them, "What time is it?"

The chief "boy" answered, "Maybe thlee time, sor," and closed the door.

"About three?" Rick looked at Zircon and Scotty. "It's early. Let's get started right away. I'd like to find out where and what the Golden Mouse is."

"Good idea," Zircon agreed. He tossed a suitcase on one of the three beds in the big room. "Let's clean up and change quickly. We'll have time to see the consul this afternoon, too. I doubt that the consulate closes before five o'clock."

In less than a half-hour the three of them were walking from the hotel toward the water front. Zircon led the way. "We'll take the ferry," he said. "It's very fast."

The ferry slip was less than a three-minute walk from

the hotel, but when they started to get tickets, they remembered that changing money had completely slipped their minds. A scholarly looking Chinese gentleman saw their plight and spoke to Zircon in faultless English with a distinct Oxford accent.

"Perhaps I can be of service, sir? If you have an American dollar bill, I can change it for you. You will need only a little money for tickets, and there is a bank close by the ferry slip on the other side."

"You're very kind," Zircon said. "We'll accept your offer, sir. I do have a dollar bill, I believe."

He found it and handed it to the Chinese, who counted out six Hong Kong dollars and a few tiny paper bills that represented change. "The rate today is six and a fraction to one," he explained.

Rick and Scotty added their thanks to Zircon's. The Chinese bowed. "A pleasure to have been of even such small service." He smiled and continued on his way.

"The Chinese are without a doubt the most polite of all the Eastern peoples," Zircon said. He pushed a Hong Kong dollar through the ticket window, got three tickets and some change in return. They pushed through the gate and walked across the dock to the ferry.

As they did so, Rick got his first look at Hong Kong. He stared, amazed, his mental image of an oriental city vanishing like a burst bubble.

Across the bay, a green mountain stretched like a jagged knife-edge against the sky line. Here and there, far above the bay, were white blocks, like granite chips, marking houses. Lower down, the city of Victoria began. It was like marble slabs piled in an orderly array, thinning out toward the upper side of the mountain. Down at sea level, the buildings were thickly clustered. But they were modern buildings, not a trace of the oriental in them.

Between the ferry and Hong Kong, the bay was crowded with water traffic. Junks with gay sails sped noiselessly between puffing little tugs. Great deep-water freighters were anchored, lighters at their sides taking off cargo. Slightly to one side, the sleek line of a British cruiser was visible, and beyond it a trio of lean, wolfish destroyers.

The ferry moved away from the pier and picked up speed. Rick and Scotty watched the colorful panorama of vessels. Hong Kong was beautiful, Rick thought. And it was clean, though cities of the Orient were traditionally dirty.

Nor was his first impression changed when they reached the opposite shore. The ferry landed them before tall, concrete buildings that shaded clean streets. A block away they stopped to watch a three-story trolley pass by.

"Good gosh, a skyscraper on wheels," Scotty exclaimed.

And that was just the impression it gave.

Zircon stopped to ask directions of a passing Englishman, then told the boys, "The American Consulate is only a block away. Suppose we change some money, then pay the consul a visit."

Rick thought quickly. "We'll need money, but why

do all of us have to go see the consul? We could split up. Scotty and I could start locating the Golden Mouse while you're talking to him."

"He probably knows all about it," Zircon pointed out. "It must be a prominent landmark, although I've never heard of it. Otherwise, Chahda wouldn't have known about it."

"Unless it was a place Bradley had told him about," Scotty said.

"That's possible. At any rate, we've nothing to lose by separating for a while. I'll go see the consul and find out what he knows. You two start asking questions and I'll meet you in an hour right here . . . no, better still, since we'll want to eat here, I'll meet you in front of Whiteaway-Laidlaw's Department Store. It's only a few blocks from here and there's a good restaurant close by."

Rick's memory rang a bell. "Isn't Whiteaway-Laidlaw in Bombay?"

"Yes. But it's also here, and in most major English cities in the Far East." The big scientist smiled. "I picked it because I was sure you'd remember the name. I wasn't so sure you'd remember Huan Yuan See's Restaurant."

"You were right," Scotty replied with a grin. "Well, let's get going. I see a bank across the street. We can get our money changed there."

It took only a few moments to exchange some of their American currency for Hong Kong dollars. The boys folded the bills, which like all English paper money were bigger than American bills, and tucked them into their wallets. Zircon started for the consulate with a wave of the hand and a reminder that they would get together in an hour.

"Now what?" Scotty asked.

"Now we start asking questions," Rick told him. They had paused at the entrance to the bank and the guard was standing near by. His turban and neatly curled beard proclaimed him to be a Sikh, a member of the warrior Indian caste that is scattered throughout the Far East.

"We're looking for something called the Golden Mouse," Rick said. "Can you tell us where it is?"

The Sikh considered. Then he shook his head. "Not know of that one, sir. Not hear."

"Maybe one of the bank officers would know," Scotty suggested. They stepped back inside the bank and approached a thin young Britisher who wore tweeds in spite of the heat of the day.

Rick put the question to him. The Englishman looked blank. "Golden Mouse, you say? Dashed if I ever heard of it. Is it supposed to be a tourist place do you know?"

"We don't know," Rick answered. "We've no idea."

The young man's face expanded in a pleased smile. "Don't suppose you'd consider substituting a pink rabbit? We have a restaurant of that name. Haw!"

Rick hid a grin. "Very kind of you," he said. "I'm afraid my friend and I are allergic to rabbit fur."

With a perfectly straight face, Scotty added, "Haw!"

The young Englishman shook with laughter. "You

know, that's really very good," he said. "Allergic to rabbit fur! Very good! I'm sorry, fellows, but I'm afraid I
can't help locate your Golden Mouse. Why not try a
bobby?"

"Bobby sox or bobby pin?" Scotty asked.

The bank officer's eyebrows went up, then he smiled.
"Oh, I see what you mean. No, it's not a joke this time.
Bobby is what we call policemen. You know?"

"Thank you very much," Rick said.

"Not a bit. By the way, I can make a few inquiries of
the chaps who have been here for some time. They may
know. If you have no luck, drop back." He offered his
hand. "My name is Keaton-Yeats. Ronald Keaton-
Yeats."

Rick and Scotty offered their names in exchange.
"We'll come back if we can't locate it," Rick assured
him.

Outside, Scotty laughed. "Haw!" he said.

Rick grinned. "That's the famous English sense of
humor, I guess. He's a good scout."

Scotty nodded his agreement. "Funny thing about
these English. They do things that seem silly to us, like
wearing tweeds in bathing-suit weather and cracking
bad jokes. But when the chips are down, they can fight
like wildcats." Suddenly he pointed. "There's a police-
man."

"Let's tackle him," Rick said, and led the way across
the street.

The officer was evidently a lieutenant or something
of the sort, because he had impressive-looking shoulder

tabs on his uniform. As they came up, he was inspecting the papers of a small, hard-bitten character who wore greasy dungarees and a cap black with grease and grime. Evidently the papers were in order, for he handed them back and said curtly, "All right, my man. But remember we'll have no doings from you or your like in Hong Kong. If you're smart, you'll stick close to your ship."

The man muttered, "Aye aye, Orficer. That I will." He moved away.

The officer was a tall, erect man with a cropped, gray military mustache. He saw the two boys and nodded. "Can I help you, lads?"

"Perhaps you can, sir," Rick said. "We're looking for something called the Golden Mouse."

The officer's eyes narrowed. "Are you now?" he inquired. "And what would you want with the Golden Mouse, if I may inquire?"

"We're to meet a friend there," Scotty said.

The tone of the officer's voice told Rick that something was wrong. He asked, "Is something wrong with the Golden Mouse? We don't even know what it is."

"A good thing for you not to know," the officer retorted. "You're Americans?"

"Yes, sir," Scotty said.

"Then the Hong Kong force is responsible for seeing that you have a pleasant and safe visit. I warn you. Keep away from the Golden Mouse."

He turned on his heel and walked off. Rick and Scotty stared after his retreating figure, and then at each other.

"How about that?" Scotty wanted to know.

Rick frowned. "There must be something fishy about this Golden Mouse. From the way he talks, it's a place. I wonder what kind?"

A cockney voice spoke from behind them. "Now, that's a thing I could tell you lads, always providin' you was willin' to part with 'arf a quid or so."

It was the man the officer had warned to stick close to his ship. He winked at them. "Come over 'ere where that blinkin' peeler cawn't see us." He motioned to the shadow of a hallway.

Inside, he grinned at them. "I 'eard the line o' garbage the copper was 'andin' you and I says, 'ere's a chance to do a bit o' fyvor fer a couple o' rich Yanks. And, I says, likely they'll part with a few bob to buy ol' Bert a bit o' tea."

Rick pulled out a couple of Hong Kong dollars. "We'll pay you. Now tell us what the Golden Mouse is, and where it is."

Bert pocketed the notes. "As to what it is, it's a kind o' restaurant, you might say. It 'as entertainment and food and drink, and you'll find a few o' the lads there for company most any night. Aye, it's a fair popular place, is the Golden Mouse." He grinned, and there was a gap where his two front teeth should have been. "As to where it is, that's not so easy to tell a pair what don't know 'ow to get around. But you just get a couple rickshaws, and you say to the coolies to take you to Canton Charlie's place. They know it, right enough."

He spat expertly at a cockroach that scuttled past.

"But take a tip from ol' Bert and don't go. Stay clear o' Canton Charlie's."

"Why?" Rick demanded.

"Never you mind why. Just stay clear. Bert's warnin' you."

"We want to know why," Scotty insisted.

Bert grinned evilly. "Right-o. The lads wants to know, and Bert's an obligin' gent. You go to Canton Charlie's and I'll make a bet, I will. I'll bet you'll be outside again in 'arf an hour, or maybe less."

His grin widened. "But will you know yer outside? Not you. And why? On account of you'll be layin' in a ditch somewheres with yer throats cut. That's why."

He pushed past and left them standing in the door-way, staring at each other.

CHAPTER VI

The Golden Mouse

HOBART ZIRCON listened to Rick's report on the boys' findings, then made an abrupt change of plans. Instead of eating in Hong Kong, they took the ferry back to the hotel and took from their suitcases the old clothes each had brought to wear on the trail, and to give them the look of experienced hunters. As Steve had pointed out, only amateurs go in for fancy togs as a rule. The experienced prefer tough, ordinary clothes like dungarees and denim shirts.

As they unpacked, Scotty asked, "Is it safe to leave our rifles, and Rick's camera and that scientific stuff you brought?"

He referred to some delicate equipment packed in a special case that Zircon had brought from the Spindrift lab for investigating the heavy water they hoped to find.

"Perfectly safe," Zircon assured him. "In reputable hotels of this sort, the Chinese help is scrupulously honest. You could leave money lying about and it would never be touched."

He had already reported on his conversation with the consul general. There had been no word from Bradley, although Steve's instructions to co-operate with the Spindrift party had arrived. The American official had promised to get in touch with them if Bradley turned up. He had never heard of the Golden Mouse.

"I think we had better try to get in touch with Chahda right away," the scientist said. "So let's have a bite to eat here, then go have a look at this Golden Mouse, or Canton Charlie's. From the description, I'd say it is typical of a certain kind of place where toughs hang out. Each city in the Orient has several. If we wear these old clothes, we'll be less conspicuous."

In a short time they were in Hong Kong again. Zircon hailed three rickshaws and they got in. "Canton Charlie's," the scientist commanded. "Chop chop."

The rickshaw boys started off at a trot. The way led along the bay shore, past wharves and piers, until they were out of the central part of the city and moving into a section that was more as Rick had imagined an oriental city to be. The streets were wide, but lined with board-front buildings. The signs were all in Chinese, and usually painted in gaudy colors. There were no Englishmen in sight now, nor did they see any policemen.

It was a long way. They had left their hotel in full daylight, but dusk had settled before the coolies finally turned off the main road. They went into a narrow street, then turned down another and still another. With each turn the streets narrowed and the light grew dimmer. How had Chahda heard of a place in such a poor quarter of the city? Rick wondered.

Presently the rickshaws drew up in a dismal corner of what was little more than an alleyway. They were in front of a low wooden building with windows that hadn't been cleaned in years. Above the double door was a faded painting, illumined by a single electric light bulb. The painting probably was supposed to represent a mouse. Once, long ago, it had evidently been yellow. Now it was so glazed with grime that it was hard to tell.

Rick stepped down from his rickshaw, sniffing the combined odors of garlic, pungent sauces, filth, and stale beer. Scotty joined him, and they waited for the scientist to take the lead.

Zircon handed some money to the coolies and ordered them to wait. Then he motioned to the boys and led the way to the door. It opened on a large room dimly lighted by faded Chinese lanterns that hung over low-power bulbs. The walls were covered with a grimy paper of faded yellow on which unskilled drawings of mice at play were clustered. The floor was crowded with tables, each table covered with a yellow-checkered tablecloth. So far as Rick could see, there wasn't a clean cloth in the lot.

In front of the room was a long bar of scarred teakwood. Behind it were row after row of ordinary ten-cent-store water tumblers. Rick guessed Canton Charlie's clients weren't fussy about drinking from fine crystal.

Next to one wall, a white man in rumpled, dirty dungarees was sleeping with head down on the table. His snores were not musical. At one of the tables near the opposite wall, a dark-skinned man in a seaman's woolen cap sat paring his nails with a knife easily a foot long.

Zircon motioned to the boys and they sat down at one of the tables. "It's too early for many customers, I suppose. But someone in charge must be here." He banged on the table, then lowered his voice. "How do you like the customer over there? A Portuguese sailor, from the look of him."

In a moment dingy curtains parted next to the bar and a man emerged. At a guess, he was Spanish.

"Bet he's got a knife a foot long, too, under that apron," Scotty whispered. "He's the type."

Rick nodded. Scotty was so right! The man's heavy-lidded eyes were set in a swarthy face whose most prominent feature was a broken nose, flattened probably with some weapon like a hard-swung bottle. A white scar across his chin indicated that it might have been a broken bottle. He was medium tall, and he wore a cap that might have been white once. An apron covered loose black Chinese shirt and trousers. Rick was glad big Hobart Zircon was sitting next to him.

The man walked to the table and greeted them in a surprisingly soft voice in which there was an accent Rick couldn't identify.

"You're a little early, gents. But I can take care of you. What'll you have?"

"Chahda," Zircon said flatly.

The man's eyes narrowed. "You better have a drink and sit tight."

"Why?" Zircon asked.

"You'll see. What'll you drink?"

Zircon ignored the question. "Who are you?"

"Canton Charlie. What'll you drink?"

"What have you got?"

There was a ghost of a smile on the scarred face. "I'll fix you up." He clapped his hands. An elderly Chinese in dirty whites shuffled out. Canton Charlie spoke a few words of singsong Cantonese and the old man nodded.

"Sit tight," Charlie said again, and walked away.

"Lot of fine, useful information we're getting out of this," Scotty grumbled. "I wonder how long we'll have to sit in this flea bag?"

"Hard to say," Zircon replied. "But Charlie seemed friendly enough."

The old Chinese was shuffling across the floor with a tray that held three tumblers of dark liquid. "Wonder what he's going to give us?" Rick said. "Probably dragon blood."

The Chinese put the glasses down in front of them and padded off again. Scotty picked up his glass and sniffed, and a grin split his face. "Dragon blood, huh? Ten thousand miles from home, in the worst dive in Hong Kong, and what do we drink? Coke!"

Rick laughed. "American civilization and the mysterious East. But it suits me. Coke is probably the only thing in the house fit to drink."

The Portuguese finished the drink that had been in front of him, gave his nails a last inspection, stowed his knife in a leg sheath, and left. He hadn't even looked at them.

"He's probably gone to find a blowtorch to shave with," Zircon rumbled. He motioned toward the door. "New customers coming."

They were the first of many. Within a half-hour the room was filled with a strange assortment. There were British, American, French, Dutch, Portuguese, and Filipino sailors, and men of uncertain profession who ranged in complexion from pure Chinese to pure black. Many were Eurasians, and of the Eurasians, a large percentage were of mixed Chinese and Portuguese blood. Zircon reminded the boys that the Portuguese colony of Macao was only half an afternoon's boat trip south of Hong Kong.

By and large, Rick decided, Canton Charlie's customers were as tough a looking bunch of pirates as he had ever seen. They applauded noisily by banging glasses on the table as a disreputable lot of musicians appeared and began to make the night hideous with what seemed to be a Chinese version of a Strauss waltz. By this time, the room was so blue with cigar and cigarette smoke and so noisy with coarse chatter in a half-dozen tongues that it was hard to see or hear one's neighbor.

Again Rick wondered. How had Chahda ever heard of this place? He sipped on his third coke and leaned over toward Scotty and Zircon. "Wonder what's keeping Canton Charlie?"

Zircon shrugged expressively. "Can't do a thing but wait, Rick."

Fortunately, the wait was not much longer. A Chinese shuffled past and dropped a folded note on the table. Before they could question him, he had made his way among the tables and was gone.

Zircon picked up the note, glanced through it, and handed it to Scotty. Rick read over his friend's shoulder. The note was scrawled in pencil, as though written in haste.

"To find the one you want, go to the end of the Street of the Three Blind Fishermen. Go to the junk with the purple sails."

"Let's get started," Rick said. He rose to his feet. Zircon tossed some money on the table. The three of them made their way through the noisy mob of roughnecks and out the door. Rick breathed deeply when they were out in the narrow street again.

"Even with the garlic, this air smells better than what we left inside," Scotty said. "Why do you think Canton Charlie didn't deliver the message himself?"

"Maybe he's not mixed up in it," Rick suggested. "Maybe he just had orders to let someone know when we showed up."

"We'll soon know," Zircon predicted.

As the three rickshaw coolies materialized from the darkness where they had been waiting, the Americans climbed in. Zircon asked, "You know street called Three Blind Fishermen?"

One of the rickshaw boys nodded. "Not far. We go?"

"Yes."

The rickshaws lurched forward.

Inside the Golden Mouse, Canton Charlie started for the table where the three had been waiting. He stopped short as he saw they were no longer there, turned on his heel, and hurried into an inner room. He spoke quick words to a slim Chinese-Portuguese half-caste who immediately hurried out the back door. Once in the open, the slim man ran as though devils were after him.

CHAPTER VII

The Junk with Purple Sails

FOR PERHAPS ten minutes Rick, Scotty, and Zircon sat in the rickshaws while the coolies pulled them through dark streets with no more noise than the occasional creaking of a wheel or the slapping of bare feet on the pavement.

There were houses on both sides of the streets, but only now and then did a light show through the impenetrable darkness. Rick finally sensed that they were near the water by a feeling of greater space around him rather than by anything he could see. A moment later he heard the lapping of water against a pier.

He was tense with excitement now. The first part of the journey was coming to an end. In a few minutes they would be hearing Chahda's story.

The rickshaws drew to a stop and the coolies dropped the shafts so their passengers could climb out. The coolie who spoke the best English asked, hesitantly, "You pay now, sor? We no wait here, yes?"

"Very well." Zircon paid the boys' fare and his own. "I don't suppose there's any reason to have them wait, since this is our destination. Chahda's friends doubtless will provide a ride for the return journey."

"I don't like this," Scotty whispered. "There's something funny about the whole business. I feel it."

"Where's the junk?" Rick demanded softly. "I can't see a thing."

"We'll wait for a bit," Zircon said quietly. "And we'll be on our guard, just in case Scotty's intuition is right."

They waited quietly, leaning against what seemed to be a warehouse, for what felt like five minutes but was probably only two. Then Rick heard the mutter of voices and the splash of something moving in the water. The sounds were followed by a bumping and scraping against the pier that jutted into the water.

"Be ready," Zircon commanded in a whisper.

As he said it, a bull's-eye lantern made circles in the night, outlining the high stern and bow of a junk. The lantern swung upward, revealing the junk's sails. They were purple.

Zircon led the way down the pier to the junk. "Chahda?" he called softly.

An accented voice answered, "Come aboard." The lantern played on the pier's edge to guide them. Following its light, they jumped from the pier into the litter of rope, boxes, and gear in the middle of the uneven deck. The stench that smote their nostrils was terrible. Probably the vessel hadn't been cleaned since it was built. Rick coughed from the foul odor and then raised his voice. "Chahda? Where are you?"

From somewhere the same accented voice replied, "We take you to him. Sit down and wait."

Rick turned in the direction from which the voice had come. He guessed that the speaker was in the stern, although it was hard to tell which was which. Then he saw a few lights along the shore change position and knew they were moving.

For no reason, he had a sudden impulse to jump back on the pier. He took Scotty's arm. "We're moving!"

"I know it. And I don't like it." Scotty's voice sounded grim.

Zircon, a huge bulk in the darkness, leaned close to them. His usually booming voice was barely audible. "Stand back to back, the three of us making a triangle. Then feel around on deck and try to find something to use as a club. I agree with Scotty. Something is very fishy here. If Chahda's anywhere within reach, he could have come himself. He wouldn't just send someone."

The boys whispered agreement. They turned, so that Rick felt Scotty's arm on his left side and Zircon's on his right. He stooped and pawed through the clutter on the deck. His groping hand found a slender piece of wood that he rejected at first. Then, when he failed to find anything else, he groped around and found it again. At best, it was a poor weapon.

They settled down to wait. The junk was just barely making headway, and as they stood waiting, their vision cleared a little. Or perhaps distant lights on the shore provided faint illumination. Rick could make out two men poling the junk from the stern.

Far out on the water came the sound of a fast-moving

craft of some sort, then a searchlight probed the water briefly. From aft came a muttered exclamation, then rapid orders in liquid Cantonese.

Scotty's elbow dug into Rick's back. "They're coming," he said tensely.

Dark figures hurtled at the three.

A flying body slammed into Rick, smashing him to the deck. He lost his stick, but struck out with his fists. He heard Zircon roar like a wounded bull.

Rick fought valiantly. Two men were on him, struggling to tie him with lengths of rope. Once he felt the rope pulled across his cheek, leaving a burning sensation. He sensed rather than heard the crashing and shouting around him. Then he wriggled out from under his assailants and staggered to his feet. Instantly one of the men was upon him again.

"Fall flat!" Zircon bellowed.

Rick did so, on the instant. There was the sound as of a baseball bat smacking a steer and for an instant the deck was miraculously clear. Zircon had found a piece of two-by-four lumber about eight feet long, and he was swinging it like a flail.

The accented voice called, "Drop it or we shoot!"

A figure swung upright next to Rick and threw something. There was a grunt and a crash as the man who had called went down.

"Got him," Scotty said with satisfaction.

A voice rattled orders in Cantonese. The polers from the stern advanced, their long poles held out like lances. Zircon was their target.

Scotty whispered, "Let 'em get close. You take the left and I'll take the right. Go under the poles."

For a heartbeat there was quiet. Rick divined the strategy. The polemen would lunge at Zircon, then the rest would leap. He didn't know how many there were of the enemy. He thought there must be at least seven. He flattened out, eyes on the left poleman, ready to spring. The poles came nearer, one was over him.

"Now," Scotty hissed.

Rick went forward, scrambling, legs driving. It was football, but easier. His shoulder caught the poleman in the stomach, and he lifted. The man went flying. Next to him he heard a dull thud, then he saw Scotty stand up, looming large in the darkness.

But the rest of the crew had charged. For a moment Zircon's lumber wreaked havoc, then he struck a part of the junk and the two-by-four splintered. He let out a yell of rage and flung himself on the nearest man, lifted him bodily and threw him at the others.

Yellow light pierced the darkness from the direction of the shore. A voice screamed, "Yanks! Over the side! Swim here!"

"Get going," Zircon howled. "I'll cover you!"

Rick took heart. He ran to the side and jumped feet first. Scotty came within a hair of landing on top of him. From overhead came cries of rage, then another bellow from Zircon. In the next instant the scientist plunged into the water with them.

"Swim for it," he commanded. He rose high out of water and yelled, "Out with those lights!"

The automobile lights that had illumined the scene blinked out. The voice called back, "Hurry! The junk is putting about!"

Rick was swimming at his best speed, head down in a powerful crawl, but he took time to look back over his shoulder. The junk was turning! He knew with despair that it could run them down easily. The shore was a long distance away. "Spread out," he called. "Then they can't get all of us." He put his head down and cut through the water like a fish. If only there were time to undress! But he didn't dare pause even long enough to untie his shoes.

The swim was a nightmare. Every few moments the auto lights blinked briefly as their unknown friend gave them a course to steer by. Rick looked back once and the junk had straightened out and was gaining on them. He redoubled his efforts. Scotty was even with him, but Zircon was pulling ahead.

He heard voices close behind and cast a glance back. The junk with the purple sails was perilously close. He drew new strength from somewhere and forged ahead.

The swimmers had closed the distance rapidly. The next time the lights blinked Rick could make out two figures standing next to the car. He could hear the creaking of gear on the junk and the grunts of the pole-men, and the sounds were close! He lifted his voice in a cry for help. "They're on top of us!"

The car lights blinked on, and held the junk in their glare. A gun fired once from the shore. Rick saw the orange spurt. Then he heard a cry from almost overhead and the junk veered sharply.

"Angle right," Scotty called, and Rick saw that they were almost at the tip of the pier. He put on a last spurt, caught a pile, and pulled himself up by its lashings. In a moment all three of them were running down the pier toward the waiting car.

The lights came on and a British voice called, "In the car. Hurry!"

"It's the bank clerk!" Scotty gasped.

It was. Ronald Keaton-Yeats ran to meet them. "Do hurry!" he exclaimed. "We think someone from this end has gone for reinforcements for your friends yonder." The three followed him to the car, a touring sedan of British make. Rick sensed that someone was behind him and started to turn, but a soft voice whispered in his ear.

"Keep looking ahead. Get to your hotel and wait there for a phone call."

They piled into the car, wet clothes and all. Keaton-Yeats ran around to the driver's seat, then stopped. "I say! Where did that other chap go to?"

"What other?" Zircon asked.

"A Eurasian. He's the one who led me here, and who fired that shot. Dashed uncivilized, but I guess it saved your bacon, rather. No matter. He's vanished and that's an end to it." The young Englishman had been peering into the shadows. "We'll hie on our merry way and leave him to his own devices."

Rick started to mention the message that had been whispered in his ear, then decided not to, although he couldn't have explained why.

The car roared into life. Keaton-Yeats spun the wheel

and they raced up the street, the buildings magnifying the sound of their passing into thunder. Not until they were on the main street was there quiet enough for conversation, then Zircon demanded, "Would you mind giving us an explanation? Naturally, we're interested."

"Rather!" Keaton-Yeats said. "I met Brant and Scott this afternoon when they inquired from me the way to a Golden Mouse. I'd never heard of the creature, as I told them, and they rejected my offer of some other sort of animal. Haw! But after they had gone, I made inquiries. I learned that this Golden Mouse was a dive of the most unsavory character."

He steered around a group of rickshaws and Rick clutched the back of the front seat. He was having a fine case of jitters, because the Englishman was driving on what appeared to Rick to be the wrong side of the road. Even when he realized that left-hand driving was the rule in Hong Kong, dodging cars on the wrong side left him rattled!

"I worried a bit," Keaton-Yeats went on. "Even made a phone call or two. Discovered Brant and Scott were registered at the Peninsular Hotel. But by the time I phoned there, they had gone out. Having no engagements, I decided to look up this Golden Mouse place and at least add another soul to the party for safety's sake, so to speak. However, I never got in, for just as I turned into the proper alley, after a bit of searching, this Eurasian chap jumped on my running board. He asked did I care to help out three Americans who were in trouble. I assured him that it would be a pleasure, but I was already committed to two Americans, in a manner of speaking. He demanded names. I gave him the two I knew. He said you were mixed up in this affair in which he was taking a hand. I told him to get aboard and he did so. We tore around odd streets for some time. My nose is insulted from the things I've smelled tonight, I assure you. We were about to throw in our cards, then, as luck would have it, we spotted three rickshaw coolies, and blessed if they didn't turn out to be yours. We sped down that Blind Fisherman Street just in time to hear the most infernal commotion out in the bay. The rest you know."

There was no adequate way of thanking Keaton-Yeats. Without his kindly interest in two strangers, they would doubtless have lost their lives. But when they told him as much, he laughed it off.

"Oh, I'm sure that's overdoing it a bit. What that crew was probably after was a bit of ransom. Pirates are still something of a problem around here, you know. We've had regular ocean-going craft picked off by them and held. I've enjoyed it immensely, and if thanks are due, I'll give them to you. Life was getting to be a bit of a bore."

And that settled it, so far as Keaton-Yeats was concerned. He drove them to the Kowloon ferry, but suggested that they take a walla-walla in view of their disreputable appearance. As they shook hands all around, he said, "Oddest thing. To me, the most curious business was that chap who watched us. Not the Eurasian. Another one. It was because of him that we suspected new recruits for our pirate friends were on the way."

"What did he look like?" Rick asked.

"Can't say. We never did see his face. Or any of him, for that matter. Somewhere up the alley was an open door, and he was standing in it, against the light. At least I believe that was the case, for all we saw was his shadow. A most unusual shadow, at that. It was so long and thin that it looked like a pole with a head and limbs. Our Eurasian friend was a bit disturbed by it, too, for he mumbled something about blowing the creature's head off if he stepped out of his doorway."

"But you didn't see anything except the shadow?" Scotty asked.

"Not a blessed thing. There was just that form, outlined in light, stretching clear across the alley. It was uncanny, because to cast a shadow such as that the bloke must have been ten feet high and no thicker than a pencil!"

They had found the Golden Mouse. Now another bit of Chahda's cable had come to life. Rick's lips formed the words.

"Long Shadow!"

CHAPTER VIII

Long Shadow

"WHEELS within wheels and all of them turning merrily," Zircon said. "I am absolutely appalled at how little we know of what is going on."

The three of them, refreshed by showers, were in the hotel dining room having a late snack.

"Anyway, we have friends working for us," Scotty pointed out. "I think our British pal did just as he said. He found out that the Golden Mouse was not the sort of place for a couple of American tourists and decided to go there in case we needed help."

Rick agreed. "And thank heaven he did. But I have a couple of questions, besides the biggest one of all."

"The biggest one being: Where is Chahda?" Scotty added.

"Right. Also, I want to know why that motorboat appearing on the scene and flashing a searchlight made the junk gang jump us."

"I'm only speculating," Zircon replied, "but mightn't

that have been a police boat on regular patrol? The junk gang would know it, I presume, and they might decide to get us tied up and under cover, just in case the police came too close."

"That's reasonable," Rick agreed. "We'll probably never know for sure, and that's as good an answer as any. Now, my next question is: Who was the Eurasian who got together with Keaton-Yeats?"

"You don't suppose it was Chahda?" Scotty suggested.

"Couldn't have been," Zircon replied. "Chahda wouldn't have faded away as soon as we got to shore. I can't imagine who the stranger was, except that he apparently was a friend. Also, I think it's clear that Canton Charlie certainly is not a friend, since our asking for Chahda resulted in our being kidnaped, or close to it."

Rick nodded. "Clear as air. Anyway, Bert's prediction was wrong. We didn't get our throats cut in Charlie's."

"He could have been only too right," Scotty reminded. "If we had gone there alone and hung around until the mob got wilder, it could have happened. What a wonderful crew of cutthroats! And they were on the way to getting set for a few fights among themselves when we left."

Rick glanced at big Hobart Zircon. "Having the professor along probably helped, too. Even the toughest thug would think twice before tackling him."

Zircon chuckled. "I must admit I've found it some advantage to be so sizable. What do you boys think of this strange shadow?"

"Strange is right." Rick stifled a yawn. "Keaton-Yeats

thought he was unfriendly, and so did the Eurasian. But he didn't do anything very unfriendly, I guess. He just stood in a doorway."

"Chahda's cable said to beware of the long shadow," Scotty remembered.

"Which is a good reason to think that the man who cast the shadow is an enemy who now knows of our presence in Hong Kong," Zircon added. He glanced at his watch. "It's getting late. If the phone call our unknown friend mentioned to Rick doesn't come soon, it'll find me asleep when it does."

"Same here," Rick agreed. "Let's go up to bed."

Zircon paid the check and they took the elevator. As they walked down the long corridor to their room, Scotty scratched his head. "Mighty funny how everything was arranged for us at Canton Charlie's, wasn't it? We drop in, ask for Chahda, wait a while, get a note, and walk right into the arms of a reception committee. That's mighty good organization."

"They had plenty of time to get the junk ready for us," Rick pointed out. "We sat in Charlie's and cooled our heels for a long while."

"We should have had knives a foot long." Zircon smiled. "Then we could have given ourselves a manicure, like the Portuguese who left right after we arrived." He put his key in the lock and pushed the door open.

Rick had a confused impression of wild sounds, then something crashed into him and he landed flat on his back. As he scrambled to his feet, plaster showered down on him, and his ear separated the sounds. From within their room, a voice screamed, "Watch out! Take cover!" There was a blurred racket, as though a giant was running a stick along a monster picket fence at jet speed. Scotty was yelling something and Zircon was bellowing with rage. Then the thunderous stitching noise stopped.

All three of them started into the room at the same time, and Rick reached the door first. It was dark in the room, but in the faint light from the hallway he saw two figures struggling. He acted without thought. On a dresser just inside the door he had left a big flashlight. He grabbed it, jumped into the fray, and brought it down on the head of the man on top. The man slumped.

With a catlike twist the man who had been underneath wriggled free. Rick started to say, "What's going . . ." Then an open hand drove into his face and pushed him backward into Scotty and Zircon. The three of them fought for balance as Rick's assailant ran to the window, leaped out on to the fire escape, and was gone.

Scotty snapped on the light just as the man Rick had slugged staggered to his feet, blinking. He was of medium height, with a thin, dark face. He was dressed like a seaman, and apparently he was a Eurasian. Black eyes blazed at the three of them.

"Shut that blasted door! And bolt it!" the man commanded.

Zircon bellowed, "Don't be giving us orders! Explain . . ."

"I'm Carl Bradley," the man said.

Rick swallowed. Of the two men in the room, he had lowered the boom on the wrong one!

Scotty shut the door and threw the bolt.

"I've got to talk fast," Bradley said. "The hotel people will be up here in a few seconds and I don't want them to find me. It would mean too many explanations, and the police would want a statement I'd rather not have to give."

He straddled a chair. "I suppose you've guessed that I was the Eurasian with the young Englishman. It was just luck I picked him up, and more luck that we found your rickshaw coolies. Long Shadow's men had you, and Long Shadow was watching. That's why I faded when you got ashore. I intended following him, for once, instead of being followed myself. About the only thing I don't know about him is his secret headquarters. I didn't think I'd be able to get here, so I whispered to one of you that I'd phone. Well, Long Shadow led me here, up the fire escape. We came by a rather roundabout route, stopping while he ate. I suspected it was your room, but I didn't know for sure. He came in. I crouched on the fire escape. Didn't know what would happen, of course. Then we heard voices. I say we— he didn't know I was here, of course. He hauled a Schmeisser machine pistol from under his coat and slipped a clip in. There was just enough light for me to see the outline. It's distinctive."

A queer little shudder zipped down Rick's spine. A Schmeisser! It was the pistol known as the "burp gun," that sprayed slugs like a hose. No wonder he hadn't recognized the sound! He kept his eyes on Bradley, intent on what the slender JANIG man had to say.

"I yelled out a warning," Bradley went on, "and jumped through the window at him. Didn't dare take time to draw my gun. I kept yelling, hoping one of you would give me a hand. He's wiry as a thuggee bandit. Only I got a lump on the head instead."

"I'm sorry," Rick muttered.

"The damage is done and he's gone. Now I'll have to locate him again, if I can. Meanwhile, write this down. Quickly. I think I hear voices coming down the hall."

Scotty whipped a pencil and an envelope from an inside pocket.

"See the consul general. I've talked with him. He will give you a rubber boat and a Nansen bottle I've picked up. Outfit for the trail, and have plenty of weapons. Fly to Chungking and check in with the consul there. Ask him to give you a reliable guide. You're going to Korse Lenken. That's in Tibet." He spelled the name. "Chahda has gone on ahead. I'll follow. That's where the heavy water is coming from, I'm pretty sure. Chahda will check up. You can help him, then make tests to be sure it's really heavy water. Maybe you can do something about the source of the stuff. You'll have to see when you get there. I've got part of the story about what's being done with the water, but not all of it."

There definitely were voices outside now. The burp gun had brought the hotel people. In a moment there was a hammering on the door.

Bradley walked to the window. "You can let them in after I've gone. Any questions? Quickly!"

"What's the Nansen bottle for?" Zircon demanded.

"I don't know. I only know that Long Shadow bought five of them." Bradley threw a leg over the window sill and grinned at them. "Leave me out of any story you tell. I need a free hand for the next few days. And the less the police know about me the better for all of us." He hesitated as the pounding on the door grew louder, then a key grated in the lock. "I can tell you this," he said softly. "You can forget about an industrial plant. This is something else we're up against."

Then he was gone.

"Open the door," Zircon said. For the first time, Rick saw that the big scientist gripped his right arm just below the elbow, a red, sodden handkerchief balled in his left hand.

"You're wounded!" He jumped to the scientist's side.

"A scratch," Zircon said. "But it saved our lives. Tell you about it later. Open up, Scotty."

Scotty threw the door open and the English night clerk, three Chinese policemen, and half a dozen coolies piled in.

"What's going on here?" the clerk demanded. "What happened?"

"Nothing serious," Zircon said calmly. "There was evidently a bandit in our room. We opened the door and he fired with his submachine gun. Then, when he saw he hadn't killed us, he fled."

It wasn't a very convincing story. Rick saw suspicion in the faces of the hotel people. He threw in his nickel's worth. "What kept you so long? We've been trying to phone." He had a hunch the switchboard coolie was one of those in the room. Probably everyone on duty had raced up.

"We heard nothing downstairs," the night clerk said. "The floor coolie came down to get us. He took his time about it. Why was your door locked?"

Zircon tried hard to look sheepish. "I guess we must have bolted it in the confusion. Then, when you knocked, we tried to open it. It was a few seconds before we realized the bolt had been thrown and the door couldn't be opened unless the bolt was withdrawn. And the confounded thing stuck."

"Why didn't you yell?" one of the policemen demanded.

"Possibly you were yelling so loud yourselves you didn't hear us," Zircon said mildly. "You were making considerable noise."

The clerk frowned. "The manager will have to hear about this," he stated. "I doubt that he will believe your story. You may even be asked to pay damages."

Zircon drew himself up to his full height. "The day we pay damages for the privilege of being shot at in this disreputable dive you fatuously call a hotel will be the day Hong Kong sinks beneath the sea like Atlantis. Now have the goodness to clear out and let us get some sleep."

The clerk's face was scarlet. Rick tried to hide a grin.

"You'll have to make a formal statement to the police," the clerk snapped.

"In the morning," Zircon said. "In the morning we intend to see the American consul. You will hear more about this incident than you expect, my dear sir. Now clear out. We need our sleep. This has been most unsettling."

One of the policemen pointed to Zircon's bloodstained sleeve. "But you need medical attention, sir."

"I happen to be a doctor," Zircon said. That was true enough, but he was a doctor of science, not of medicine.

"You expect to treat yourself?" the clerk asked incredulously.

"Nothing to it," Zircon boomed. "A trifle. Why, once, when hunting in Africa, I had my back clawed by a lion. I stitched the wounds up myself."

The clerk was on the verge of a stroke. "You couldn't treat your own back," he almost screamed. "Impossible! How could you?"

"He turned around so he could see what he was doing," Scotty said. "Good night, all." He shepherded them through the door and closed it.

For a moment there was excited conversation from outside, then the clerk, the policemen, and the coolies retreated down the hall.

"They'll be back," Zircon said wearily, "but not before morning, I hope."

Rick looked at Scotty. "He turned around so he could see what he was doing," he repeated. "My sainted aunt!"

"Sewed up his own back," Scotty gibed. "Professor! You told that nice man a fib!"

"Great big juicy fib," Zircon said gravely. "Do I wash out my mouth with soap or do I get a medal?"

"Medal," the boys said, and laughed heartily.

"Whatever got into you?" Rick asked the scientist.

Zircon stripped off his coat and rolled up his sleeve. "He was so pompous and so serious that I just couldn't resist. Besides, if I had been serious, we never would have gotten rid of them. Here, Rick. I'll need antiseptic and a gauze compress for this."

The boys looked at the wound. As Zircon had said, it was trivial. The slug had made a neat furrow across the surface of the skin, just deep enough to cause a good flow of blood. The wound already was clotting.

As Rick bandaged the scientist's brawny arm, Zircon said, "I recoiled instinctively when Bradley yelled. But not far enough. One slug just nicked me. But those heavy caliber weapons, like our service .45, will knock a man down anywhere they hit him. This one spun me around and I piled into you two. I think that is what saved us all."

"I didn't know what was happening," Rick said.

"Neither did I," Scotty agreed. "I've seen Schmeissers before, but I've never heard one fired until now."

"And let us hope we don't have to hear it again," Zircon added. When Rick finished bandaging his arm, the professor went to a suitcase and opened it, drawing out a folded map. "I'm curious about Korse Lenken," he said. "It's a new name to me. This map covers China and a part of Tibet. We may find it."

After a long search, Scotty whistled. "Here it is. And look where it is!"

Korse Lenken was a tiny dot in the vastness of the mountains just beyond the Chinese border at about 95°

east longitude and 32° north latitude. No other town was noted on the map in the area, but high mountains were, and so were rivers. And Chahda was there, alone! At least Bradley had not mentioned any companion who traveled with the Hindu boy.

"We'll need to outfit completely," Zircon said. "Food, warm clothing, sleeping bags, and all the rest. And we'll need a rifle for Rick. We can get American rifles here. Also, I think we had better put in a small supply of ammunition beyond what we brought."

For a short while they speculated on the trip, and on the many things Bradley had left unsaid. It was unfortunate that they couldn't have had a few moments longer. But Rick could see that his presence in the room would have needed explaining, since he hadn't traveled up on the elevator. It was better for him to disappear.

Before getting into bed, they went to the door and opened it. Across the hall, Long Shadow's burp gun had made a fine mess. Plaster hung in patches and the laths behind were broken and splintered. Fortunately, the room opposite was a storage closet, so no one else had been in the line of fire. Rick looked at the dozens of holes and shook his head.

"If we'd been right in the doorway," he said, "we would now be so full of holes they could use us for mosquito netting—if the holes weren't so big." He looked at the other two and added, "I'm beginning to think Long Shadow doesn't like us.

CHAPTER IX

The Trail to Korse Lenken

Sing Lam-chiong dug heels into the flanks of his mule and trotted back to where Zircon, Scotty, and Rick were jogging along on their respective mounts.

"Good place to make lunch, in about ten minutes."

"Fine, Sing," Zircon said. "We could use lunch." The scientist looked down with distaste at his horse, a big hammerheaded black with the lines of a plow beast. "This creature is about as comfortable as a wooden sled."

Rick sympathized. His own nag, a pin-eared Chinese pony of a peculiar mouse-gray color, had no particular gait. He just waddled along, swaying from side to side and making his rider saddle sore.

Sing saluted and went back to the head of the column, which was made up of pack mules, each led by a Chinese bearer. There were four of the pack animals, each laden with the party's gear.

"He certainly knows this trail," Scotty commented.

"A good thing," Rick said. "The camping places are few and far between. I wish Korse Lenken were nearer."

The party was ten days out of Hong Kong, high in the mountain ranges that formed the backbone of south Asia. Since leaving the more civilized part of China they had trekked through alternate valleys and mountain passes, making good time in the valleys, but slowing to a snail's pace in the mountains. Sometimes the trail was wide enough for the three of them to ride abreast. Sometimes it clung to the mountainside with scarcely room for a single horse or mule. But Sing, leading the way, had a knack of picking the easiest route.

The Chinese guide was a gift from heaven. The Spindrifters had checked in at the American Consulate at Chungking, as Bradley had instructed them, and the consul had offered the loan of one of his own staff. Sing, normally a clerk at the consulate, had been born and brought up in the western reaches of outer Sinkiang Province, and he knew the area from wide travels with his father, a Chinese border police officer. Although he had never been to Korse Lenken, he had been close to it.

In a short while Sing called out in Chinese to the bearers and they followed him into a sort of pocket in the mountainside. Scotty, who was slightly ahead of Rick and Zircon, turned. "We've got company for lunch. There's another party already here."

In a moment the three Americans were greeting a portly Chinese who rose to greet them.

"Howdy, Mr. Ko," Rick said cordially. "We were

wondering when we would catch up with you again."

Worthington Ko smiled and bowed. "We will doubtless meet many times until our paths separate. Please dismount and join me. My bearers have a good cooking fire you are welcome to use."

Ko was a textile merchant they had overtaken on the trail a short distance out of Chungking. Since then the two parties had passed and repassed each other several times. Ko had three mules, in addition to the one he rode, and two bearers. The mules carried only light packs. On the return trip, he had told them, they would be laden with Tibetan textiles. He was heading for the famous monastery of Rangan Lo to buy embroidery from the Buddhist monks. Eventually, the embroidery would find a market in Europe.

The three Spindrifters got down stiffly from their horses and found seats among the rocks next to the merchant. He smiled sympathetically. "You are stiff? These trails are very poor and one must travel them many times before one gets used to them." He took off his thick, horn-rimmed glasses and polished them on a scrap of silk. "After twenty years of it, I still find myself bent with weariness at the end of the day."

Sing busied himself with getting food ready. The Spindrift bearers unpacked utensils and their own rations of rice and dried meat.

Ko rose from his rocky seat and rearranged the long, flowing silk coat he wore. "I must be off. With your permission, I will proceed slowly, however, so that you will overtake me before nightfall."

"Of course," Zircon said. "But may I ask why?"

Ko's nearsighted eyes peered at the rifles carried in saddle sheaths on each of the three horses, and at Sing's shotgun. "I hope to take advantage of your weapons," he explained. "By nightfall we should reach Llhan Huang, which is a sort of crossroad. It marks the start of the Lenken country. The Lenkens are unlikely to attack a well-armed party of eight. But they delight in robbing a small party such as mine. For that reason, I usually manage to find a larger group to which to attach myself when entering the Llhan region." He smiled. "The armament you carry for hunting bharals will serve admirably to keep the Lenkens at a distance."

The Spindrift party had been warned that the tribe known as Lenkens were dangerous to travelers.

"We'll be delighted to have you join us," Zircon assured him.

Rick was about to suggest that the portly Chinese merchant wait until after the Spindrifters had eaten so they could all travel together, but he thought better of it. Ko had been cordial, but he had shown little interest in the American "hunting" party and Rick thought he probably preferred to travel at his own speed and in his own way.

Sing called that lunch was ready and they took mess kits to the fire and loaded them up with rice covered with a savory sauce, canned beef, and hot, crisp water chestnuts. As Rick sighed with gratitude over the first tasty mouthful, Scotty looked at the vanishing Ko party and mused, "Wonder how come he speaks English so perfectly?"

Sing overheard. He grinned. "No reason for surprise.

Many Chinese are educated in American and English colleges both in China and in other countries. Like myself. I am a graduate of Oberlin."

"Guess that's right," Scotty admitted.

"Worthington is a rather strange name for a Chinese, Sing," Rick remarked.

The guide nodded. "It is. But I don't think it is his real one. Many Chinese take western first names, especially those who trade with westerners. That is because our own names are often too hard to say or remember."

"Have you ever met Ko before?" Zircon asked. "Since you've traveled widely in this region, I thought you might have come across him before."

"I don't think so," Sing replied. "But this is a very big country and there are many travelers like him."

Sing was certainly right in saying that there were many travelers, although the merchants like Ko were a minority. There were families of Tibetans walking along the trail, laden with their possessions, heading for goodness knew where. There were groups of horsemen, dressed in the quilted clothes of the mountain country and with peaked felt hats. Such men usually were armed with old-fashioned muskets and carried forked rests in which to lay the musket barrels for support while firing. There were parties of Chinese, sometimes on foot and sometimes with trains of mules or yaks, the oxlike Tibetan beasts of burden.

Frequently, especially in valley country, small villages lay near the trail. Often there were herders with their large flocks of sheep.

Although the trail slanted up and down, from valley to mountain pass and back down again, the way led constantly higher toward the white-capped peaks that have been called "The Backbone of the World." Beyond them, many hundreds of miles away, lay Nepal and India.

It was always cool now, and the Americans and Sing wore windbreakers and woolen sweaters. The bearers donned padded long coats. At night, the sleeping bags were comfortable; without them the Americans would have been chilled through and through.

"Make a guess, Sing," Rick requested. "How many more days to Korse Lenken?"

Sing counted on his fingers. "With fortune, maybe we'll get there late day after tomorrow. Depends on the trails."

Zircon sipped steaming tea standing up. He was too saddle sore to sit down. "Where do we camp tonight?"

"A mile or two past Llhan Huang. I know a good water supply there."

The bearers were standing around waiting patiently, already finished with cleaning up and packing, except for the Americans' teacups. They downed the last swallows of tea and handed the cups to Sing, then swung into the saddle again.

"I hope Sing is right about getting there day after tomorrow," Rick said as he shifted uncomfortably in the "chafing seat," as he called it. "This hay-burner is no luxury liner."

"Ditto," Scotty agreed. "Besides, I'm anxious to see Chahda."

Hobart Zircon nodded. "I hope whatever we find is worth the discomfort of this trip." He grinned. "At any rate, it's a new experience for all of us."

"I don't think I'll thank Bradley for it, though," Rick added. "Well, let's get moving."

He dug his heels into the pony's flanks and moved into position behind Sing. Scotty and Zircon fell back to bring up the rear. Although they were reasonably sure no one would attack them, Zircon felt it was best to have a rear guard and they had taken turns at the end of the column.

In spite of saddle soreness, Rick looked at the view with appreciation as the trail suddenly topped a rise. Far below spread a lush valley. Beyond were the last peaks they would have to cross before they came to Korse Lenken.

CHAPTER X

The Ambush at Llhan Huang

It was late afternoon before the Spindrift caravan left the rocks of the mountain pass and reached better ground. They paused on top of a small, pyramid-shaped hill while one of the bearers retied the pack on his mule.

Zircon looked at the formation with interest. "An old volcanic cone," he pointed out. "Notice the regularity of the slope? And we're in a kind of saucer that once was a live crater."

Rick could see it clearly once the scientist mentioned its volcanic origin. The saucer was perhaps a dozen yards across, and its edge was marked by a definite rim. Whoever first made the trail apparently had decided to go right up and across the hill instead of pushing through the dense underbrush at its base.

In a moment they started again, the mules picking their way carefully down the hillside. At the bottom of the hill was a rather dense forest, and beyond it the valley.

Sing called back over his shoulder. "Llhan Huang is just past the woods. We'll meet Ko there, I think. I just saw the last of his mules going into the woods."

Rick stood up in his stirrups and rubbed his raw and aching thighs. The three had ridden horseback before, but not to any great extent, and the long trail was a hard initiation.

He noted that the sun was dropping behind the western peaks, and he knew from experience that it would be dark in a few minutes. The great western range was so high in the air that it brought night by blocking out the sunlight surprisingly early in the afternoon.

Then he rode into the forest and gloom closed in around him. It was cold. He zipped up his windbreaker and reached for his gloves. He saw that the trail through the forest twisted and turned to miss the big hardwood trees, so that sometimes he could see only the mule in front of him. Zircon and Scotty, at the rear of the column, were out of sight most of the time.

It grew darker rapidly. Rick reached into his saddlebag and drew out a flashlight, tucking it into his jacket pocket where it would be handy. When he could see the sky overhead, it was dark gray and he knew night was close at hand.

Presently he found himself peering through the gloom even to see the mule directly in front. When they got out of the woods it would be lighter, he hoped.

Then, as he stood up again to ease his saddle burns, the woods around them were suddenly alive with gunfire! His pony reared and would have bolted if he had not gripped the reins tight and jerked him to a stop. He caught a glimpse of orange flashes in the gloom, and from ahead he heard a sudden scream from one of the mules.

Scotty's voice rose in a yell. "Turn around! Turn! Get back out of the woods to the hilltop!"

Rick saw his friend's strategy at once. On the hilltop, they could fight off almost a battalion. He pulled his quivering pony around on the narrow trail and yelled at Sing.

The guide's voice came in answer. "Coming! We're coming!"

A slug whined past Rick's ear and slapped into a tree trunk. He tried desperately to get the rifle out of his saddle sheath while controlling his fear-crazed pony. Then he heard the roar of Sing's shotgun. There was no sound of firing from Scotty and Zircon, and he guessed they were having trouble with their mounts, too. None of them was horseman enough to fire from the saddle.

Rick stopped trying to get the rifle free and bent low, urging his pony on. Behind him, he heard the pound of mule hoofs, and in the woods on both sides the rustle of underbrush as the attackers tried to keep up. The shots were fewer now, thank goodness!

In a few moments the racing column broke out of the woods into better light. Ahead, Rick saw Zircon and Scotty go over the rim of the volcanic hill, and within seconds saw them reappear again on foot, rifles in hand.

"Come on," Scotty yelled. "We'll cover you!"

Zircon's big .45–90 spoke with a decisive slam and

Rick heard the heavy slug crash through the brush. Then the mules ahead of him topped the hill and in a moment he was out of the saddle, too, rifle in hand.

He joined Scotty and Zircon in time to see Sing and the other two bearers race up the hill. One mule was missing.

"Hold your fire," Scotty said. "There's nothing to shoot at unless you see a muzzle flash."

Sing jumped from his mule's saddle and took command. He spoke rapidly to the bearers, who at once forced the mules to their knees and then over on their sides. "So they won't get hit," Sing explained. "We lost one mule." He reloaded his shotgun, his face worried.

"Did you see anyone?" Rick asked.

"No. But I'm afraid for Ko. We had almost caught up when they started shooting. I saw one of his mules right ahead of me."

"Let's hope he found some sort of cover," Zircon said. He glanced at the sky. "It will be completely dark within a few minutes. Sing, scatter your men around the rim. They can keep watch, even if they have no rifles. The rest of us can take up positions at equal distances from each other around the rim."

Scotty adjusted his rifle sights. "Afraid of an attack after dark, professor?"

"I am. This attack probably was timed to catch us in the woods in the darkness. We're fortunate that Scotty's memory is good. Suggesting the hill was a wonderful idea."

"I knew we'd be cut to pieces in the woods," Scotty said.

Rick surveyed the terrain anxiously. Sing was posting his men. "A good thing they're not very expert shots," Rick said. "They took us completely by surprise."

Scotty walked to the rim and found a position that suited him. "Not much danger of their hitting us except at point-blank range, if their guns are like some of those we've seen."

Zircon found a position, too, and Rick searched for one that he liked. He finally chose a place where a broken rock pile would give him cover. It was so dark now that he could scarcely see.

There were plenty of noises down the hill, but no firing. Rick waited, rifle thrust out before him. Were they gathering for a rush? And who were they? Then he heard the noise of a dislodged pebble on the hillside below him. He strained to see, but it was too dark. He thought: If only I had the infrared light and the glasses! They were in one of the packs. Stupid not to have thought of them at once, he berated himself. Now he didn't dare leave his position until he found out what was below.

There was the sound of a body sliding over low brush almost directly beneath him. He tensed, then as an afterthought, he reached into his pocket and brought out the flashlight. With it, he thought, he could blind the attacker and at the same time get a shot at him. He put his thumb on the button and waited.

In a moment a figure loomed out of the darkness only a few feet away. Rick sucked in his breath and half lifted his rifle for a one-hand shot. At the same moment, he pressed the flashlight button.

The beam shot squarely into the face of Worthington Ko!

Rick put down his rifle quickly to extend a helping hand to the merchant. And then he noticed something.

Shoot a light into the eyes of a man whose pupils are dilated by darkness and there is a definite reaction. If the eyes are normal, the pupils contract sharply.

One of Ko's did. Rick saw them, magnified by the thick glasses. The other pupil didn't change at all.

And as the fact registered, Rick saw something else. In one of Ko's hands was a grenade!

In the instant that Rick grabbed up his rifle and swung it like a club, he guessed the answer.

Ko was the Chinese with the glass eye!

CHAPTER XI

The Goatskin Water Bag

SEVERAL things happened almost at the same time. The attackers awoke to the fact that Rick's light made a good target and started shooting. Rick dropped the flashlight as his rifle, swung with one hand, barrel forward, connected solidly with the top of Ko's head. Scotty jumped to see what was happening.

The grenade rolled from Ko's hand, and as it did, the safety handle flew off! Ko already had pulled the pin!

A musket slug cracked into the rock inches from Rick's face and sent chips of stone into his face. He felt a sudden pain above one eye. But before he had time to realize what had happened, he was hauled back bodily into the crater by the guide.

Scotty, who had recognized Ko in the beam of the fallen flashlight, grabbed the merchant by the collar and dragged him into the saucer with them.

There was a five-second fuse on the grenade, but things had happened so fast there was a second to spare

101

before it went off. Then for an instant there was a dull flash and the *cruuuump* of the grenade. Shrapnel sliced through the woods below, bringing yells of fright.

"The camera," Rick gasped. He got to his hands and knees, shaking his head. There was wetness across one eye that he thought was blood.

Scotty got his meaning instantly. He snapped, "Sing. Keep an eye on Ko," and ran to the pack animals. It took him only a moment to find the camera and lift it from its case, then he handed Zircon the special glasses and quickly fitted his infrared telescopic sight onto his own rifle.

Rick got to his feet, keeping the injured eye closed, and fumbled through the gear until he found his tripod. He set it up quickly and mounted the camera on it. Then he carried the unit to the edge of the saucer and pushed the button that lit up the infrared light. He couldn't see to shoot, but he could operate the camera unit. Through the special glasses, Zircon would be able to see anything the infrared beam hit. Scotty would be able to see, too, through his special telescopic rifle sight. Rick panned the light across the woods below. It wasn't light that could be seen, of course. Only the dull glow of the filament, too dim to be seen more than a few feet away, told him that the camera was operating.

"I see one," Zircon bellowed suddenly, and the words were echoed by the dull, authoritative slap of the .45–90. The heavy slug drove through the brush below. "Missed," the scientist said in disgust.

Scotty's rifle cracked sharply. Scotty didn't miss. There was a yell from below, then the noise of many men running through the underbrush. Rick guessed that the attackers didn't like the weird sharpshooting in the darkness.

In a few moments there was quiet, and the infrared light found nothing but the silent woods. Sing, who had been crouching over Ko, ready frying pan in hand, said, "They've gone, I think. These hill people don't like night fights, anyway."

"That's my guess, too," Scotty agreed.

Zircon found his own flashlight, and, ducking low, shot it over the saucer's edge. He waited long moments, but nothing happened. Had the men who attacked them still been in the woods below, they certainly would have fired at the tempting target.

"Bring that light here, will you, professor?" Rick called. "Something hit me in the eye awhile back." He tried to keep the concern out of his voice. Had he been blinded in that eye?

Scotty and the professor hurried to him in some concern. Zircon shot the light into his face and he blinked with his good eye.

"Good heavens," Zircon said softly. Then, on closer examination, he sighed with relief. "A scratch, just below the eyebrow. The eye itself isn't damaged. Scotty, find the first-aid kit, please? We'll have this cleaned up in a jiffy."

While Scotty held the light, Zircon cleaned the wound and washed the blood from Rick's eye. Then, in the midst of the operation, there was a metallic clang from where Sing stood guard.

Scotty flashed the light over in time for them to see Worthington Ko stretch limply on the ground. Sing's smile flashed. "He was waking up. I didn't want to bother you, so I made him sleep some more."

Rick had to chuckle. Their efficient guide had bashed Ko with his frying pan.

Zircon completed giving Rick first aid. "That's clotting nicely, Rick." He cut a tiny piece of sterile gauze and affixed it with a bit of tape. "There you are. Good as new by morning. I suspect that a chip of stone must have struck you."

Rick tested the action of his eyelid on that side. The gauze felt ten times as big as it actually was, but it was all right. "Thanks, professor," he said. "Now, let's take a look at our captive."

Worthington Ko's slumber, induced by Sing's mighty frying pan, was not very deep. A cupful of water in the face brought him around readily enough and he peered up at the Americans. He had lost his glasses in the shuffle, and without them there was no doubt that he had one glass eye. He peered balefully from the good one.

"What," he demanded, " is the meaning of this?"

"We might ask the same," Zircon stated, "except that we can assume that you sponsored the attack on us. What we want to know is, why?"

Ko snorted indignantly. "Nonsense! I was coming to your aid, having made my way through that mob of

Tibetan bandits." He rubbed his head. "And then someone struck me."

"Were you going to use that grenade as a calling
card?" Rick asked caustically.

Ko opened his mouth to speak, but Rick continued,
"Don't try to tell us you were going to use it in our de-
fense. Men don't pull the pins on grenades until they're
ready to toss them. That one had our name on it."

Ko shrugged. "I see you've convinced yourselves.
It's useless for me to say anything further." He shut his
mouth obstinately, nor could they get anything further
out of him.

Zircon motioned to Sing. "Tie him up. Then post
guards. We'll stay here for the night." He turned to the
boys. "I think it's safe to make a fire. We can have some
supper and then turn in. I'll take first watch with one
of the bearers. Scotty will take the second, Rick the
third, and Sing the last." He opened the chamber of
his rifle and extracted the shell, then put the rifle down.
"I'm hungry," he said, grinning. "Nothing like a good
fight to work up an appetite."

Scotty laughed. "You talk like a Marine," he said
admiringly.

The night passed without incident, and the entire
party was awake at dawn. Over breakfast, they discussed the affair again. Like the discussion of the night
before, it proved futile. There were simply too many
questions that had no answers.

Rick summed it up. "We've found Long Shadow and
the Chinese with the glass eye. Or rather they've found

us. And it's obvious they're out for blood. It scares me to think of what would have happened on the junk if the Englishman and Bradley hadn't taken a hand."

"I'd like to know how they knew we were coming," Scotty said.

Zircon drained the last of his coffee. "I don't think they did know. We walked into Canton Charlie's and asked for Chahda. We put the finger on ourselves, so to speak. They probably assumed that anyone asking for Chahda was an enemy. Obviously, they had some sort of contact with Chahda, otherwise he wouldn't have cabled the descriptions after stating that he was in danger."

"That sounds right," Rick agreed. He looked over to where Worthington Ko was having a cup of tea under the watchful eye of Sing. "What do we do with our fat chum?"

"Keep him for a hostage," Scotty suggested.

Zircon shook his head. "A good idea, but not practical. It would require that we guard him constantly and that would be a nuisance. No, I think we had better leave him and push on for Korse Lenken as rapidly as possible. Now that we know our danger is from Chahda's enemies and not from casual bandits, we are forewarned."

"Then what do we do with him?" Rick asked.

"Leave him here, afoot. His friends probably will find him, but I don't think that matters. Now that we know him, he's less dangerous. We can treat him like any other bandit."

Rick and Scotty agreed. As they drew nearer the goal,

both of them were increasingly anxious to get to Chahda, to hear from him some of the answers to their questions, and finally to get down to the business of finding the heavy water that was the reason for their quest.

Although they hadn't discussed it, Rick was worried about Chahda. Normally, he had full confidence in the Hindu boy's ability to take care of himself. But this time Chahda was far from the kind of people he knew, among unfriendly strangers. Was his friend hiding somewhere in the mountains around Korse Lenken? Or had he found a hide-out in the village itself?

They would soon know.

After breakfast, Rick, Scotty, and Sing surveyed the scene of the ambush, leaving Zircon to guard the Chinese and to direct the repacking of their gear.

There were definite signs of the enemy's presence in the woods below. One area was pretty well trampled, indicating to Scotty's trained eye that the ambushers had departed in a big hurry. The Chinese guide pointed to where ants were swarming around a section of ground.

"Someone was hit there," he said. "Ants find bloodstains fast in this country."

"We were aiming low," Scotty said. "Probably a leg wound. Sing, where do you suppose Ko's mules are?"

The guide shrugged. "Pretty sure to be far away. The men who attacked us wouldn't leave mules behind. They're too valuable."

Scotty led the way down the trail to where the first

shots had been fired. The three moved cautiously, just in case the attackers were waiting a little distance away. Scotty's rifle was ready for instant use.

"I was right here," Sing said. "Ko's mules were ahead of me, just a few yards away. Let's go ahead some and take a look."

The trail wound through the woods for a little distance and then broke into a clearing. Rick saw gear littered over the ground and pointed to it. "Looks as if they left something behind!"

In a moment they were looking through what was evidently Ko's entire luggage. Sing kicked at a pile of cooking utensils. "They took the mules but left everything else."

"Funny they'd do that," Rick said thoughtfully. "After all, Ko was the boss. He must have arranged the ambush. Unless we're wrong about him."

"I don't think we're wrong," Scotty denied. "You hit it on the nose when you said a man doesn't pull the pin on a grenade unless he's ready to toss it. Ko must be the boss."

Sing examined a richly embroidered robe. "My guess is that Ko hired a few Tibetan bandits. They wouldn't worry about him or his belongings after being met by heavy resistance. And his bearers would be afraid to stay and face him. Or maybe they thought he was killed while attacking us. There was a lot of noise, and it was dark."

Rick thought Sing was probably right. He walked over to a pile of furs. "What are these?" he asked. "Ko must have been a fur trader."

Sing looked up. "Water bags. Goatskin. Very common in China." He dropped the robe and came to look, his face wrinkling into a frown. "But usually a man doesn't carry so many. Very funny."

Rick and Scotty examined one with interest. It was a whole skin, except for head and feet. Even the tail was still attached. The ends of the legs had been sewed up, but the neck was left open. Attached to the neck opening was a rawhide thong that could be used to bind the opening tight when the skin was filled with water.

"These are good bags," Sing said. "Better than most."

"Perhaps he planned to sell them," Rick suggested.

"Don't think so." The Chinese guide shook his head. "People here make their own. Every time they kill a goat for meat, that's a new goatskin. The Buddhist Tibetans, who don't kill anything, even flies, use pottery jugs."

Scotty had started counting the bags. He paused at the ninth and held it up. "This one is split open. Looks like the seam gave way. There's a sort of funny lining."

Rick took the skin and turned it inside out. It was smooth and glassy on the inside, and the substance was completely transparent because he could see the skin underneath.

Sing felt of it. "Never saw anything like that before."

Rick held it to his nose and sniffed. It was odorless. He took his pocketknife and scraped at it while the others watched. A tiny flake shaved off. He tested it between his fingers, and it was flexible as rubber. An idea was growing in his head.

"It's crazy," he said. "But you know what I think this is? I think it's plastic!"

"The professor can tell us," Scotty suggested. "Come on. Let's take it to him."

They ran back up the trail, Rick leading with the skin. If the stuff were plastic, it could mean only one thing. He lengthened his stride.

Zircon looked up from his notebook as they topped the hill and ran toward him. He dropped the book and jumped to his feet, reaching for his rifle.

"It's not another ambush," Rick panted. He held out the skin. "It's this. Professor, what is this transparent stuff inside?"

Zircon took the skin and ran his finger tips over the lining. He held it up so that it caught the light, then looked at Rick curiously. "That's odd," he muttered. "This is certainly a goatskin. And almost surely, this is a plastic lining. I can't be sure, of course, but I've never seen anything like this in nature."

"It's a goatskin water bag," Rick said excitedly. He pointed to Ko. "He had a dozen of them."

Zircon bellowed, "So! Then if this is plastic . . ."

"It was a clever stunt," Rick finished. "No one would suspect coolies toting goatskin water bags. And even if anyone did suspect, he wouldn't be able to tell anything by a casual examination."

Sing scratched his head. "Forgive my stupidity," he said. "The suspicious one wouldn't be able to tell what? If this lining is plastic, it is a senseless waste. Water keeps cool in a goatskin bag because of evaporation through the pores. It certainly couldn't evaporate through plastic."

"No," Zircon agreed. "That is the idea. They don't want evaporation. Also, the plastic guarantees the water's purity."

Sing said no more, but he was obviously puzzled. Nor could the Americans tell him what had excited them, that they had found the means by which the substance they sought was carried to the coast.

Rick had a quick vision of Chinese coolies making their slow way through the countryside, unnoticed because water-bearers were so commonplace. But the coolies in this case carried bags lined with plastic, and the stuff that made the legs thrust out stiffly and that swelled the bag was not ordinary water! It was the stuff which had brought them halfway across the world.

CHAPTER XII

The Buddhist Monk

THE PARTY topped a high rise and stopped, spellbound at the scene that spread before them. They were on the rim of a great valley. Far on the other side of the valley stood the high peaks of the Himalayas, a mighty screen between them and India.

Below, a lush green path marked the course of a wide river. On either side of it, sloping up to the mountains, was the lighter green of grasslands.

Sing pointed. "There is Korse Lenken."

Rick had to look hard before he saw it. Then he began to make it out. The monastery was built under a great cliff on one side of the valley. At first glance it seemed like part of the cliff itself. It was huge, with tier after tier of gray stone buildings rising in piled masses from the valley floor. Around it, like tiny mounds of earth, were the hair tents of the Tibetans.

"Magnificent," Zircon rumbled. "Well worth coming

to see, even if we find nothing at the end of the trail."

"We'll find Chahda," Scotty said. "I'm sure we will. And the sooner the better."

Rick felt the same way. Now that the end of the trail was in sight, excitement was rising within him. He was anxious to find his Hindu friend and to find at the same time answers to some of the mysteries they had encountered.

"Let's hurry," he said impatiently.

Sing shouted at the bearers and the party took a narrow trail that dipped into the valley. Scotty rode ahead with Sing, and his rifle was ready for instant use. Rick and Zircon brought up the rear, their own rifles held ready. They had taken no chances since the fight on the hilltop. Worthington Ko had been left afoot far behind them, but there was no assurance his friends hadn't come to the rescue with horses. Rick kept glancing behind him, just in case of an attack from the rear.

They had reached the rim of the valley by midmorning. All through the day they made their way down the mountain, reaching the valley floor about three in the afternoon. Another two hours of steady travel took them past the yurts of Tibetan herders—conical tents made of horsehair felt. The stolid Tibetans watched them pass, no interest in their beady eyes.

Then, as darkness began to set in, they reached the monastery. Korse Lenken towered above them, already shaded in twilight. From somewhere within the great pile they heard the tinkle of bells, then the deep tones of a mighty gong. Lamas, priests in yellow robes, walked past with bowed heads. Some of them spun their prayer wheels and intoned the Buddhist ritual.

Om Mani Padme Hum. Hail, the jewel in the lotus!

The jewel, of course, was the Lord Buddha.

They watched the pageant for a few moments, enthralled. Then Zircon commanded Sing. "Find someone you can talk to. We'll want to see the High Lama."

Sing nodded. "I will go into the monastery. The bearers will find a place to camp." He issued orders in Chinese.

The bearers scattered at once, searching for a suitable place to pitch camp. The three Americans sat their horses and watched the activities around the great monastery, too interested even to talk.

Rick saw countless yellow robes on the various balconies. There must be thousands of monks, he thought. And there were an equal number of Tibetans, many of them already busy at cooking fires near the base of the gray stone buildings. He smelled mutton cooking, and the acrid, unpleasant odor he had learned to identify with yak butter. Hot buttered tea was a Tibetan staple. He had tried it on the trail, because he was interested in everything, even yak butter. But he didn't think it would ever take the place of ice cream in his affections.

One of the bearers came back and motioned to them. They followed as he led the pack mules to a place in the shelter of a great rock. The other bearers were foraging for wood. In a few moments a fire was going and camp was being set up.

Sing returned. "No one may see the High Lama,"

he reported. "He is in the middle of some kind of ceremony that takes a month. But I talked with an important priest. He was friendly. He said he would send one of the lamas to be our guide and to help us find your friend."

"Good," Zircon said. "Now, let's have some dinner. I'm famished."

The boys echoed his sentiments.

It was fully dark before they ended their meal. They were squatting around the fire, sipping coffee and listening to Zircon's description of the Buddhist ritual when one of the bearers suddenly called out. The three Americans and Sing reached for their weapons as a yellow-robed lama shuffled out of the darkness.

This, evidently, was their guide. He was of less than medium height, but that was all Rick could tell about him. His loose robe draped around his body and his cowl was pulled up, hiding his face.

"Welcome," Zircon boomed. "Sing, speak to him and tell him we are grateful for his coming."

Sing spoke to the monk in Chinese.

The robed lama stood immobile, just within range of the firelight. The yellow flames made shadows across his cowled figure. Rick felt a little shudder run through him. The quiet figure was somehow weird.

Sing shifted to another language, but the lama made no reply. Then, slowly, he brought his hands up level, outstretched toward them. He chanted slowly, his voice muffled under the cowl. Then the chant died and his hands were lowered once more.

Sing turned to the group. "I don't know what he said. It's not in a language I understand." He spoke to the apparition. The monk stood motionless.

"Wish they'd sent us someone we could talk with," Scotty grumbled. "A lot of use this joker will be!"

The monk's cowl turned slowly toward Scotty. The figure moved majestically toward the boy, then the hands lifted again. From under the cowl a sepulchral voice issued.

"Could be more use than you think, muttonhead."

For an instant there was stunned silence, then Rick and Scotty leaped for the robed figure with yells of delight. Rick hit him high and Scotty hit him low. They held him down and pulled the cowl from him, then pommeled him unmercifully, while Zircon cheered them on.

Only when the monk begged for mercy did they let him up. He tossed the robe aside and grinned at them.

"Okay," Chahda said. "You win. But it took you plenty time to get here! Why you take so long?"

The slim Hindu boy hugged them solemnly, one at a time, and shook hands with Sing. "Now," he announced, "I eat. Got plenty sick of sheep meat, you bet!"

Then they were all laughing and talking at once while the cook hastened to prepare a meal. In a few moments Chahda was attacking a high-piled plate and talking between bites.

"Good you came now," he said. "I got plenty worry. You find Bradley?"

Zircon told him of the meeting in the hotel.

Chahda nodded. "Good. I think he show up soon."

"Start at the beginning," Rick demanded. "There's a whole lot we don't know. In fact, if you come right down to it, we don't know anything."

"Okay." Chahda took a sip of coffee. "I start at start. In Bombay."

Chahda had been visiting with his family in Bombay when Bradley arrived in the Indian city. The two had met by accident. Chahda had gone to the Taj Mahal Hotel to write a letter to the boys, because there was no paper or ink at home. Bradley, who happened to be in the lobby, had noticed the address on the envelope as Chahda handed it to the desk clerk.

Once the scientist discovered that Chahda knew the Spindrift group and had been on expeditions with them, the rest followed naturally. Bradley, realizing that the clever little Hindu boy would be of great value in his undercover work, had hired him. Chahda didn't say so, but Rick could understand that such was the case.

Chahda's duties had been those of general assistant. He had cared for baggage, run errands, acted as secretary, and on a few occasions had been assigned to follow people in whose destinations Bradley was interested. The two had gone from Bombay to New Delhi and Calcutta, then to Singapore. At Singapore, while following up another matter, Bradley accidentally had discovered that heavy water was being sold.

"He was much excited," Chahda said. "I did not know why. Heavy water? I asked myself what is heavy water. I knew about ice, which is frozen water and which is heavy. But who would have much excitement about ice? The Sahib Bradley hurried to the Consulate of America and he sent a cable to Washington."

Then the scientist had assigned Chahda to watch a certain house in Singapore, the place from which the heavy water was being taken to unknown destinations. Chahda had watched for three days without relief, and he had seen Worthington Ko. Then, since Bradley had not come for him, he deserted his post long enough to return to their quarters, a room in an obscure Chinese hotel in Singapore. There he had found evidence of a fight and bloodstains on the floor. There was no sign of Bradley.

It was then, Chahda guessed, that Long Shadow had found him. He saw the shadow several times while he hunted for Bradley. Then, while searching for his boss in the Tamil quarter, he had been attacked by Chinese thugs led by Worthington Ko. They had beaten him into insensibility, hustled him into a taxi, and were carrying him somewhere into the inland of Malaya when he regained consciousness. He escaped by going headlong through a window while the car was traveling and then taking cover in the jungle alongside the road. Going by a roundabout route, he reached Singapore again. There he found that their luggage was held by the hotel and the room had been rented to someone else.

Chahda polished his plate with a biscuit and groaned expressively. "I say to myself then, Chahda, now is time to think real hard. What to do?"

He knew that the cable Bradley had sent asked for

Hartson Brant to be assigned to the job. And he knew also that from Singapore they were to head for Hong Kong. He knew nothing about Hong Kong, but he did know that Bradley was acquainted at a place called the Golden Mouse because he had heard him mention it to a Chinese the scientist used for undercover work now and then.

"The Long Shadow came again while I was thinking," Chahda continued. "I saw it in front of the hotel. So I went quick-fast out the back, and ran through many places until I was sure he could not find me. I went to where many Indians live in Singapore, and I found a friend."

The friend, another Indian, had gone to the United States Information Library in Singapore and borrowed a copy of *The World Almanac*. Chahda already had decided he would cable the boys, and how he would do it. He knew, because of what they had told him, that they would be able to figure out a book code and that they would realize his choice naturally would be the *Almanac*. Knowing the annual by heart, he naturally also knew the table that converted Roman numerals to Arabic numbers and had used the letter L as a clue to the right volume.

"But how did you know about nulls?" Rick asked.

"Oh, that was very lucky. I learned how to put Sahib Bradley's messages in code, and there were many nulls." He grinned impishly. "Of course I did not know if you also knew what are nulls. I was thinking, they are two who are good with science. But are they also good with code? Maybe not. But, anyway, they are plenty smart to read a book. That will tell them about nulls."

"We didn't have to read a book," Scotty said. "Dad told us about them."

"Scientist father also plenty smart even without books," Chahda agreed. "Anyway, I make the message and I send cable."

Rick interrupted again. "How did you know Ko had a glass eye?"

Chahda smiled. "When they capture me, I fight like maybe ten wild elephants. I kick honorable Mr. Ko in the face. And what happens? His glasses fall off and one of his eyes falls out! Also, it breaks when it falls and I see it is glass. I am so surprised I forget to fight and someone hits me from the back of my neck, and then all is dark. I did not know Mr. Ko's name then. My boss tells me it later."

"No more questions for the moment," Zircon ordered. "I want to hear the rest of this. Go ahead, Chahda."

The Hindu boy had used his friend as a go-between and had arranged for the consul general to advance him funds. Since the official knew he worked for Bradley, that was not difficult. Then he had arranged for their baggage to be shipped and held at the airport in Hong Kong, and had taken a plane there himself.

At the Golden Mouse, Canton Charlie had given him quarters. In another day, Bradley showed up. The scientist had been caught in the Singapore hotel room by Ko and company, but had fought his way clear. There wasn't time to leave a note for Chahda at the hotel and he didn't dare return to the room for fear of having the enemy locate him again. So he had depended on Chahda's wits to tell him the next step and had gone ahead to Hong Kong, hoping to find more information about the heavy water.

At Hong Kong, Long Shadow had shown up again.

Bradley, in the meanwhile, had not been idle. Through his various sources of information he had determined that the source of the heavy water was in the neighborhood of Korse Lenken. Chahda was instructed to go there at once and start reconnoitering while they waited for the party from the States. Bradley deliberately dropped the disguise he had been using, that of a Portuguese seaman, and let Long Shadow locate him. Then he had started out, hoping to draw the enemy away from Chahda long enough for the boy to get clear and start for Korse Lenken. Bradley was to shake the enemy when he could and resume his investigation. Finding the source of the water was not enough, he had said. It also was necessary to find out how it was reaching Singapore, and what its ultimate destination might be.

Chahda had experience with Buddhist monasteries dating back to the time when he had worked in Nepal. Also, many Indians were Buddhists. There were some in almost every monastery, and of that number a few could be depended on to speak Hindi, or Hindustani as it was called, which was Chahda's language. He also knew a little Tibetan from his years in Nepal.

"I came here easy," Chahda finished. "There was a big lot of pilgrims and they took me in." He grinned.

"They thought I was a monk. And I found Indians, like I had thought. They hid me, so I do not think Long Shadow knows I am here. And now I know where the heavy water comes from."

Zircon gave an exclamation. "Chahda, you're a marvel! Where does it come from?"

"Tomorrow I show you," Chahda promised.

"Who is Long Shadow?" Rick demanded.

Chahda shrugged. "Not knowing. We never see him. Only the shadow."

Scotty stirred up the fire a little. "How come Canton Charlie didn't turn you over to the enemy as he did us?"

"What?" Chahda was astonished.

Scotty quickly outlined their adventures while Chahda listened thoughtfully. When he had finished, the Indian boy shook his head. "Something bad wrong. Charlie is one of Bradley's men. My boss pays him, and he is friendly. You say Charlie told you to go to this junk?"

Rick thought back. Charlie himself actually had not told them. They had not seen Charlie when the note was dropped on their table.

"Charlie himself didn't tell us," he stated. "It could have been one of Long Shadow's men. Or one of Ko's. And that Portuguese with the knife could have been one of Long Shadow's men, too. I'll bet he was the one who put the finger on us. He must have heard us ask for Chahda. Long Shadow and his men knew Chahda, of course, and they would certainly try to get rid of reinforcements like us."

"Right," Zircon agreed. "Perhaps the fault was ours in not waiting for Charlie to tell us himself, although I don't see how we could have known."

"I think that is it," Chahda said. "Charlie is a friend. So the men on the junk with purple sails were Long Shadow's, and you plenty lucky you get out with your skins, believe me."

Zircon rubbed his chin. "Chahda, our instructions from Bradley were to bring a rubber boat and a Nansen bottle. That must mean the heavy water source has something to do with a lake or river. Is that true?"

"Don't know about those things," Chahda said. "I know only that the heavy water comes from a place near here. I know how to get there and I will take you. I do not think we will like this place much. It has a bad name."

"What kind of bad name?" Scotty asked.

"In English," Chahda said, "it is 'The Caves of Fear'!"

CHAPTER XIII

The Black Buddha

LONG ago, according to the tale Chahda had heard from his Indian Buddhist friends in the monastery, a High Lama and some of the chief priests of Korse Lenken forsook their vows and went in for piracy with the monastery as headquarters.

For years they flourished, robbing travelers and even swooping down on Chinese cities across the border. The name of Korse Lenken was known throughout the East as a place of terror. Between attacks, the High Lama and his priests made mockery of the religion of Buddhism that they were sworn to uphold, and they built a huge caricature of Buddha, all in black and with the face of a demon.

Then, went the legend, as they dedicated the great statue to the hordes of the mountain underworld, the Lord Buddha himself appeared in the sky and stretched his hands over them. The vast multitude of robbers fell to their knees and lifted their hands for mercy. And

Lord Buddha, the gentle and merciful, gave them mercy. His voice rang through the mountains like the winds of heaven: "Live! Live unharmed. But live in fear! It is written."

Buddha, so went the legend, then vanished. A great wind sighed through the valley, and bolts of light flashed from heaven. It grew black, black as the darkest night. And when the blackness cleared and the wind died, new mountains stood where the High Lama and the multitude had been.

The lamas who had remained faithful to the teachings of Buddha labored to build a new monastery, and as the years passed they heard mutterings in the earth. Then one day a repentant lama, who had been one of the multitude, came forth, an old man. The High Lama and the robbers still lived, he said. But they lived in the blackness under the new mountain, in vast caverns where no light ever came. And there were *things* in the darkness. Things they could not see, but of which they were terribly afraid. As Lord Buddha had said, they lived in fear.

The little group was silent as Chahda finished reciting the legend. Then the Hindu boy added, "Of course this is long ago. So very long. Maybe it is only a story. And maybe not. The monks of Korse Lenken do know there are big caverns, and they know of this Black Buddha. I know of it myself. But more than that I do not know."

"And it is from the Caves of Fear that the heavy water is presumed to come," Zircon finished. "That is quite a tale, Chahda. But how do we get to the Caves of Fear?"

"The entrance is somewhere in the Cave of the Black Buddha," Chahda said. "At least, that is what the monks have told me. Also, they showed me how to get there. But I did not go in." He shuddered a little. "Who knows if the old High Lama might not be waiting? I thought better I wait for you."

Rick felt the weirdness of the tale, too, but he made a joke. "I didn't think hobgoblins would frighten you away, Chahda."

Chahda didn't smile. "People who live in the East do not laugh at hub-gubbles, Rick."

"I was just trying to be funny," Rick apologized. "Well, what do we do now?"

"We look in the caverns for the source of the heavy water," Zircon stated. "And the sooner we start, the better. Chahda, have you seen men with water bags heading out of here? Men with anything at all suspicious about them?"

The Hindu boy nodded. "I have seen such men. Once I saw ten men going up the trail to the outside with such bags. The bags were all they had. I am sure the bags had heavy water. If not, why so many?"

Zircon told him of the plastic-lined bags they had found and of their suspicions.

Chahda saw the implications instantly. He grinned. "We find out plenty more about these water bags, you bet! I think I go right now and find out if any more men with bags go by today." He hurried off, getting into his monk's costume as he went.

Rick watched him go, shaking his head with admiration. "He's a wonder," he said. "I'll bet Bradley thinks so, too."

"Anyone would," Scotty agreed. "He gets things done. Wish I could say the same for us. All we've done so far is travel while he did the work. Why don't we get busy?"

"Busy how?" the scientist asked.

"Couldn't we look into this cave tonight? I don't see that waiting until morning will help much. If it's a big cave, there won't be light in it, anyway."

Rick thought Scotty had something there. He pointed out that plenty of lights were in their packs, and that they had the dark-light camera besides.

Hobart Zircon thought it over, then agreed. "There's another advantage," he added. "Starting out tonight, we'll attract less attention. We got here about dark, so the people of the area don't know we're here. They'll know in the morning, though, and we'll have a thousand sight-seers hanging around, unless they're greatly different from the other Eastern people I've met. And the less anyone knows about our interests, the better."

Sing nodded agreement. "That is right. By morning many people will come to see the strangers. I doubt if they have seen very many white men before." The Chinese guide paused. "But I don't know if I like the idea of going into strange caves while it's dark. As your little friend says, anything is possible in this part of the world. Even hobgoblins."

"We wouldn't want you to come, anyway, Sing," Rick said. He looked at Zircon for agreement. "It would be better if you took care of our equipment and sort of acted as rear guard. We'll need someone to stand by in case we don't come out of the cave again."

"Afraid the hobgoblins will kidnap us?" Scotty asked.

"Not hobgoblins. But if the heavy water is there, some of Long Shadow's men will be, too. We probably can take care of ourselves. Only suppose they catch us by surprise?"

Zircon agreed. "Rick is right. And even if there is no one in the cave, there remains the possibility of accident. I think we'll do well to leave Sing here. Then, if we're not out in twenty-four hours, he can take steps to get us out."

"That's wise," Sing nodded.

They were debating what to take with them when Chahda returned. He reported that some of the lamas had seen men with goatskin water bags late in the day, men that they knew to come from outside the valley, traveling from the general direction of the Cave of the Black Buddha. It was such water-carrying groups that had made Chahda sure that the cave was the source. There was no other near-by place that was possible.

"That settles it," Rick said. He told Chahda what they had in mind.

Chahda glanced at the sky. "Moon in a little while," he said. "With no moon, we could not even get there. Too rough. But if no clouds come, we can go."

Rick was a little surprised that Chahda hadn't objected in view of his apparent dislike of the whole idea. Then he realized that the little Hindu boy wasn't made that way. He might be afraid, but he would go. That was true bravery.

After some discussion, they decided not to take their full equipment, but merely to use the trip to locate the entrance to the Caves of Fear. Once the way was found, they could return and load up with gear and provisions. However, each of them took a few emergency rations, a full canteen of water, their weapons, and flashlights. Chahda was given a big electric lamp to carry. Rick slung the dark-light camera over his shoulder while Scotty changed his rifle sight for the infrared telescope.

The moon was up by the time they were ready. They shook hands with Sing and started off, Chahda leading.

The way led across the valley at a slight angle, heading toward the river. At first it was smooth going, with only high grass underfoot. Rick was enjoying himself. The moon gave light to the valley center, but the sides, under the sheer mountain walls, were shrouded in shadow. The peaks themselves, snow-capped to the west, were bright.

Then Chahda cut back away from the river toward the nearest mountain wall. The way began to get rougher, with hillocks to climb and rocky outcroppings to skirt.

Soon they were out of the grassland entirely, walking through rock masses. Now and then they went from the moonlight into dense shadow and had to use their flashlights. Except for their flashlights, no man-made light disturbed the wild scene. They had been traveling for some time. It was late and not even a fire in front of a herder's tent could be seen. By Rick's watch, it was almost eleven.

It was closer to midnight when Chahda stopped. He pointed to a rocky defile. "This is as far as I went before. My friend who showed me said the cave is there."

Zircon took the lead. Behind him, Rick put his own flashlight away and held his rifle ready for use. Scotty, too, was ready. Chahda, crowding Rick's steps, had the big light ready to turn on.

Zircon's beam picked out rocky walls that rose for a hundred feet. He picked his way over tumbled rock, the others following. The way took a sharp turn, then came to a dead end.

"Nothing here." Zircon's light covered the area a foot at a time. There was no opening.

"Maybe we missed it," Scotty suggested. "Let's go back, and examine everything on the way."

They reversed their steps. All of them used lights now, and the combined beams illumined the steep walls brightly.

"Take a look at that," Scotty said suddenly. His light was on a pinnacle of rock that appeared to have some sort of opening behind it. He moved in, cautiously, the others close behind. There was an opening, sure enough, where the pinnacle leaned against the main rock wall. There was just barely room to squeeze through. Zircon almost got stuck.

Once past the opening, a new trail seemed to open up. And at its end an aperture in the rock wall loomed black before them.

"That must be it," Rick said, and his voice echoed hollowly.

Scotty moved ahead to the entrance and flashed his light inside. The beam was lost in the blackness beyond. "It's big," he said, and the words rolled around in the emptiness.

Rick felt a shiver run down his back. "What are we waiting for?" he demanded roughly. "Let's get inside."

The opening wasn't large. Zircon had to duck going in. Rick was right behind him, Chahda bringing up the rear. Just inside, they stopped, all lights going.

The cave was tremendous. The level rock floor stretched away from them, and when they shot their lights upward, a vaulted dome reflected the beams a good hundred feet overhead. Slowly they moved away from the entrance, lights busy searching the cave. There was nothing near the entrance but rock, solid and smooth. And it was so quiet Rick thought he could hear his own heartbeat. Then his light beam picked up a green reflection on the far side of the cave.

"There's something there," he exclaimed. In spite of himself, his voice shook.

"We'll soon see," Scotty said. Their voices rumbled through the cave, echoing and re-echoing.

Zircon gave a sudden exclamation. "Chahda! Where's the big light?"

The Hindu boy had been playing the bright beam on the walls to one side. Now he swung it squarely ahead, and Rick gasped.

The Black Buddha!

It seemed to crouch against the far wall, a giant, loathsome thing of dead black with live green eyes.

They went toward it, all lights on the thing, and as they made out more details, Rick shuddered. The Buddha was completely the opposite of every other Buddha he had seen. Instead of the bland, quiet look of peace, this thing had its mouth open, showing sharp ebony teeth. It leered over a nose like a pig's, and its body was gross and misshapen. It was, Rick thought, toad-like. It quite frankly gave him the willies. His imagination gave it life, so that the obscene lips smirked, and almost seemed to drool.

Something white at the base caught the light beams. In a moment they stood before a pile of bones, heaped against the statue's left side.

Zircon's light swept them. "Human," he said.

Rick's scalp tightened.

Next to him, Chahda let out his breath in a sigh that was nearly a moan.

In the second that they stood silently looking at the pile of bones, there came a slight sound from somewhere behind the Black Buddha. Instantly their lights swept in the direction of the sound, until Scotty hissed, "Put 'em out!"

Blackness flooded in on them. Rick strained his eyes to see, his ears to hear. He tried to control his breathing, sure that its sound could be heard forty feet away.

Then he saw a horizontal thread of light about three feet long against the wall behind the statue. It spread upward slowly, forming a rectangle. Rick watched it,

his palms wet on the rifle as he tucked the flashlight
away and gripped the weapon tightly.

It was yellow light, eerie as a will-o'-the-wisp and
scarcely stronger. Then, as Rick watched, a shadow rose
up in a black narrow path from the bottom of the rectangle. It rose and rose until it almost filled the frame,
and the blackness was in the form of a man, almost, except that it was too long, too thin.

The four stood as though hypnotized for a dozen
heartbeats, then Zircon came to life. He jumped forward
with a great roar.

"Long Shadow!"

The light vanished and again blackness closed around
them.

CHAPTER XIV

The Caves of Fear

INSTANTLY all lights were directed at the back of the cave. Zircon rushed around the statue and stopped short as his light found only rock walls.

"He has to be here somewhere," the scientist bellowed. "Hunt for him!"

Rick stood for a moment estimating the direction from which the light had come. He walked to the part of the wall on which they had seen the shadow, and stood with his back to it. He flashed his light straight ahead, and it fell on the broad back of the Black Buddha.

The others had followed his line of thought and were watching.

"Look for a door," Scotty said. He hurried to the back of the statue and began examining it with his light. Rick joined him. Zircon got out a jackknife and began to probe into cracks. Chahda got down on hands and knees and felt along the base.

134

The back of the statue was seamed with cracks, but they ran helter-skelter without apparent order. The illumination against which the shadow was cast had been rectangular.

"There isn't a straight line in the bunch," Rick said, disappointed. "What now?"

"There must be a way to open the door, wherever it is," Zircon stated. "That's what we must look for, I think. It may be on the statue itself, on the floor, or on a wall near by. Rick, you and Scotty take the statue. Chahda and I will take the walls and floor."

"What are we hunting for?" Scotty asked.

"I don't know. Perhaps a knob, perhaps a keyhole. Look for anything unusual."

Rick and Scotty began at opposite sides of the statue's back and started working toward each other, examining every inch of the black stone minutely. Zircon and Chahda started side by side on the wall behind the statue and worked away from each other. Rick used his jackknife to probe every suspicious crack or chip, but without success. He and Scotty covered the back as high up as they could reach without finding a thing. Zircon and Chahda worked along the wall until they were thirty feet apart, then the scientist called a halt on the theory that the secret lock wouldn't be that far from the door. The door was either in the statue's back or near its base.

While Zircon and Chahda started examining the floor, Rick and Scotty started on the statue's sides. There was more decoration along the sides, so they had to go more slowly and carefully.

After a while, Chahda called, "Something here."

The others stopped what they were doing and hurried to him. The Hindu boy's light was on a tiny slot in the floor. It seemed shallow. Rick pointed out that the floor in the area was checkered, almost like a tile floor.

"There must be a reason for that," Zircon said. He knelt by the slot and peered into it. "Nothing in the slot, however. Rick, isn't yours a scout knife?"

"Yes, sir." Rick handed it to him.

Zircon opened the screwdriver blade and pushed it into the slot. Nothing happened. He moved it from side to side, with no effect.

"There must be some reason for that slot," Scotty said. "Try again, professor. Push harder."

Zircon shoved the blade down into the hole and pushed. "There must be a special key of some kind," he said finally. "That is, if the slot has anything to do with the door. I suggest we continue the search until we're satisfied that this is the only possibility."

Rick nodded, disappointed. He turned back to the statue and took a step forward into space!

A wild yell burst from him as he felt himself falling, then Scotty had him by the jacket and was hauling him back. Rick collapsed on the stone floor, his heart pounding. The others shot their flashlights into the place where he had stepped.

A section of the floor had swung upward, right at the base of the statue. It yawned open, and from its lip a flight of steps led downward.

"It worked," Chahda said. "But was so silent we never hear it!"

Scotty gripped his rifle and snapped off the safety catch, then holding the weapon in one hand like a pistol, he took his flashlight in the other hand and started down. Zircon was right behind him.

Rick got to his feet and felt for the dark-light camera. It hadn't been jarred because his body had cushioned it. But he wanted to be sure the strap was still secure on his shoulder. Satisfied that all was well, he started down the steps after Zircon. He didn't fancy going into the underground part of the cave, but there was no choice. This was what they had come for.

There were ten broad stone steps carved from the rock. Rick shot his light around and saw that a heavy beam ran from the underside of the trap door down to the bottom of the stairs where it ended in a stone block. It was a counterbalance, the weight of the stone evidently just enough heavier than the door so that moving the latch would let it swing open. The latch itself was a piece of metal, probably bronze, that slid in a channel carved in the underside of the door. Rick guessed that the sideways pressure of the blade in the slot had let the door open rather than the downward shove Zircon had given. A cord of leather ran from the latch back along the corridor so that anyone entering the rock tunnel could tug on it and open the door without climbing the stairs.

Rick joined Zircon and Scotty at the bottom of the steps. Chahda was right behind him. The stairs ended in a long, low passage, just high and wide enough for a man to pass. It was perhaps fifty feet long, and it ended in blackness that indicated a bigger passage, or another cave, beyond. Rick touched the walls and noted the marks of ancient chisels. The passage had been cut in the living rock.

"Have your rifles ready," Zircon directed. "Chahda, you have the big light. Lead the way and we'll cover you."

Chahda switched on his big light and took the lead. The others, rifles ready for instant use, followed close behind. Big Zircon held his weapon over Chahda's shoulder as the Hindu boy walked slowly down the passage.

In a moment they were at the entrance to the next passage or cave. Chahda peered in, turning his light from side to side. Zircon, looking over his head, said, "A large cave beyond. Very large. Chahda, do you see anything?"

Chahda shook his head. "Only rock. Nothing inside I can see."

"All right. Go ahead."

The Hindu boy stepped into the cave, the rest following. Rick saw that Zircon hadn't exaggerated. The cave was even larger than the one that held the Black Buddha. Chahda's big light picked out the opposite wall dimly.

The scientist brought his own light into play, turning it on the walls nearest them. "Odd," he muttered. "The character of the rock changes completely. This is almost surely limestone."

Rick had to grin. Even chasing Long Shadow through an underground cavern couldn't quiet Zircon's scientific curiosity. "What do we do now, professor?" he asked.

Zircon looked up from his examination of the whitish rock. "Eh? Oh. Sorry, Rick. Why, I suppose we explore a bit more. I don't think we'd better go far, however. Now that we know that Long Shadow is here, we had better return to camp and get extra food, batteries, and ammunition. However, I would like a look at the opposite side. There must be further passages, because this cave obviously doesn't contain our friend."

"Suppose . . ." Scotty started to say.

Rick never found out what Scotty was going to say, for at that moment the four whirled as something grated behind them. They were in time to see metal rods slam home across the entrance through which they had come!

Rick and Scotty reached the entrance first. Each of the boys grabbed one of the rods and tugged. They were rigid.

"We're locked in!" Rick's voice was harsh.

"Let me look," Zircon said quietly.

The boys stood back while he made a careful inspection. From floor to top of the passage entrance the metal bars blocked the way. They were about an inch thick, spaced only six inches apart. They had shot out of holes in one side of the passage and lodged in corresponding holes on the opposite side.

None of them had noticed the holes. They had been too curious about what lay beyond the passage.

Zircon put his massive strength against one of the

bars. It didn't move. He tried to slide it either way. There wasn't even a fraction of an inch of slack.

He turned, and at the expression on his face a shiver slid down Rick's spine. Long Shadow had caught them neatly.

They were trapped in the Caves of Fear!

CHAPTER XV

The Labyrinth

ZIRCON led the three boys to the center of the big cave, then spoke in a whisper. "I see no need in advertising our plans to the enemy. Keep your voices down. Now, what are we to do?"

"Long Shadow must be watching us from somewhere," Scotty said uneasily. "But from where?"

"The walls are uneven," Rick pointed out. "There could be peepholes anywhere. But what I'd like to find is the place with the controls for that gate! It can't be far from the entrance."

"Is true," Chahda agreed. He turned the big light on the barred entrance, then played it back and forth across the walls on that side of the cave. There was no break anywhere.

"Turn it on the other side," Zircon ordered.

Chahda did so. Now that they were closer to the far wall, openings could be seen. There were two, both of them door size. Except for the entrance through which

141

they had come, they were the only openings in the cave.

Rick spoke up, and he was surprised that there was no shakiness in his voice. "Look, gang. If we stay here waiting for Long Shadow to open up, we might stay forever. I'd rather push on, at least for a little way."

Zircon looked at Scotty. "You're the military expert. What chance have we in a fight?"

Scotty shrugged. "In an open fight, we have a good chance. Our rifles are better than any I've seen around here, and we can fire a lot faster. But if they start potting at us from around corners and through holes in the rock . . ." He didn't have to finish.

"Better we go ahead," Chahda said.

Zircon hesitated. "If this is the only entrance to the caverns, as seems quite likely, Long Shadow has trapped himself as well as us. He'll have to open up to get out."

Rick didn't think so. "There's no opening under the Black Buddha except the one we came through. But we didn't look around the passage very thoroughly, so there might be a door of some kind."

"You're right," Zircon agreed. "Very well. Let's try going on. Rick, you bring up the rear, and keep looking back."

Rick objected. "Wouldn't it be better for me to go ahead and use the infrared beam with the glasses? Then I could see perfectly."

The scientist considered. "It would be better if the caves ahead are large, yes. If they are not, our flashlights will do just as well. I think we'd better save the infrared battery as long as possible. Incidentally, do you have a spare?"

"At camp," Rick said. It had been planned as a brief trip of exploration. He hadn't thought spare batteries would be necessary. Now he blamed himself for being so shortsighted. It was always best to be prepared for anything.

"Can't be helped now," Scotty said. "And speaking of batteries, we'd better use only two flashlights at a time, one in front and one in back."

"Excellent idea," Zircon approved. "I'll take the lead. Scotty next, then Chahda, with Rick as rear guard. Now, which of the entrances do we try first? I vote for the one on the right."

The scientist strode toward the deeper darkness of the entrance and shot his light inside. The others took up the positions he had assigned. Rick kept his flashlight beam moving around the big cave, watching for any sign of an enemy.

"Another passage," Zircon said, and his voice echoed hollowly. "Cover our rear, Rick." They went into it single file, Rick walking sideways in order to keep looking back for a possible enemy. Then, as the others stopped suddenly, he fell over Chahda. He heard the scientist say, "Dead end. Nothing but a blank wall. Rick, lead the way out. We'll try the other."

The second passage gave better results. It wound through the limestone for a short distance, then opened into a small cave filled with wonderful white rock formations.

"Stalactites and stalagmites," Zircon boomed. "I suspect we are getting into the deeper caverns, those hollowed out by water and not by man. The question is, which way do we go now?"

Rick took his eyes from the way they had come long enough to look around. The cave was like a junction room, openings branching off in all directions.

Scotty switched on his flashlight and began examining the cave floor. "Look for sign," he directed. "If men have come this way, they must have left some traces."

Chahda hurried to look, too. Rick stood where he was, light and eyes going from one opening to another. He didn't intend to be caught off guard.

Scotty gave a grunt of satisfaction and stood up. "Candle wax," he announced. "And it leads through here." He pointed to a gap between two fluted columns, made by centuries of dripping water that had deposited countless grains of limestone.

Zircon immediately walked to the gap and peered through. "Come on," he said. "There's another cave beyond."

The next cave was larger, and nowhere in it was there evidence that man had occupied it. Rick looked around him, awed by the bizarre beauty of the place. From ceiling and floor limestone icicles strained toward each other. They were the stalactites and stalagmites Zircon had mentioned, formed over the centuries by slow drops of water, each of which left its tiny trace of limestone to help build up the formation. On one wall of the cave the water deposits had carved a waterfall, so perfect that it might have been frozen into white rock only moments before. And from every grain of stone their flashlight beams twinkled and reflected until it seemed the walls were crusted with jewels.

"More wax," Chahda called. He had found it near an irregular low opening in the cave wall, a tiny drop left by someone carrying a tallow candle.

Zircon went through the opening an inch at a time, on hands and knees. The others followed, to find themselves in a cave almost identical to the one they had left, except for the stone waterfall. This cave, too, had walls broken in a number of places.

Rick and Zircon flashed their lights around, seeking the next step. Then Rick caught a quick glimpse of something red that moved! Quick as a flash he shifted his hand on the stock of his rifle, pointed it like a pistol, and fired. The red object vanished!

The thunderous echo of the shot reverberating through the cave drowned out his yell. He sprang through the entrance where he had seen the flash of red and found himself in still another cave. Scotty was right behind him.

"What is it?" Scotty demanded.

"I think it was a man," Rick said quickly. "He was wearing something red. Come on, he can't be very far from here."

"Which way?"

There was no way of telling which way the man had gone. There were a half dozen openings in the cave walls. Rick pointed at the two biggest. "You take that one and I'll take this." Rifle ready and flashlight held in front of him, he ran through the break in the wall he had indicated. Scotty hurried to the other.

If only they could get their hands on even one man, Rick thought, they might force him to serve as their guide! He passed through another cave, choosing the biggest entrance on the opposite wall. As he went through it, he was certain he saw a movement, as though the quarry had just rounded a corner. He let out a yell and lengthened his stride. In a second he reached the corner, rounded it, and found himself in an odd cave with countless pillars, formed when stalactites from the ceiling and stalagmites from the floor had joined together. It was a veritable labyrinth. He started through it, got perhaps fifty feet, and stopped. The man he had chased surely knew his way around the caves. There was no hope of overtaking him now. Better rejoin the others, Rick thought. It was senseless to get too far away from his companions.

He turned and started back, then hesitated, not sure of the way he had come. The corridors formed by the limestone pillars led in all directions.

"I must have come this way," he muttered, and started off. Then he stopped again, playing his light around. He couldn't be sure. Suddenly worried, he ran forward and was brought to a halt by a solid wall. He turned and hurried along it, seeking an opening. He found one, but smaller than the one through which he had come. He plunged on, found a big opening, and went through it into an irregular cave unlike any he had

seen before. He turned to retrace his steps, and his eyes
met a wall where the openings were separated only by
glistening partitions of limestone. He couldn't even be
sure of the one through which he had just entered.

He licked lips that were suddenly dry. "I can't lose
my head," he told himself sternly. "I've got to stay
calm."

But in spite of his warnings to himself, he felt panic
rising within him.

He was completely, hopelessly lost!

CHAPTER XVI

The Lake of Darkness

Rick sat with his back against the cold surface of a stalagmite column. His head drooped with weariness and his throat ached from yelling. He had retraced his steps a dozen times or more. He had lost count. But none of the passages took him back to his friends, nor had his yelling of their names brought a response.

He forced himself into a semblance of calmness and tried to think. What was he to do? He eyed the beam of his flashlight and realized that he ought to conserve the batteries. He turned it off, and dead, silent blackness closed in about him.

True blackness is rare. It cannot be found by closing shutters or curtains in a room, even at night. Some light always penetrates man-made rooms unless they are designed, as very few are, for total darkness. Rick never had experienced it before, and it was frightening. He had to take a firm grip on himself to keep from getting panicky.

But if the underground caverns were completely

without light, they were not completely without sound. As Rick sat quietly he began to hear the slow drip of water. It was the slow drip of centuries that had produced the weird limestone formations of the caves.

He began to talk quietly to himself, and the sound of his own voice was better than listening to the slow dripping of water.

"I can't stay here. The others wouldn't have any more chance of finding me than I have of finding them. But if I leave here, I'm taking a chance. I might go so deep into the caves that I'd never find my way out again, or see any of the others again."

He had visited some of the limestone caverns of Virginia, and he had read of the New York and Kentucky caverns. He knew that even in America there were endless series of caves that never had been fully explored. This fabled Tibetan place might extend on forever.

"On the other hand," he continued to himself, "if I keep moving, I might stumble on the big cave under the Black Buddha again. It's less than a fifty-fifty chance. A whole lot less. But it's a chance and I'd better take it."

He didn't let himself think of what would happen if he failed to find his way back. He got to his feet and switched on his light again. By contrast with the total darkness, the reflection of the beam on the limestone walls was brilliant sunlight. He had to wait while his eyes adjusted themselves to the light. Then he flashed the beam around. There were passages going in every direction.

"Which way do I go?" he asked himself.

It was a tossup. He remembered an old trick and spat into the palm of his hand. Then, with the forefinger of his other hand, he slapped the spittle sharply. The biggest drop flew between two limestone hourglasses that formed one passage. He hitched up the camera case on his shoulder, picked up his rifle, and started forward.

The caverns were endless. Walking slowly, to conserve his strength, he wandered through countless incredible rooms of gleaming stone. The dripping water had formed all manner of things. He saw animals, ships, mountain scenes, waterfalls, and cataracts, fairy grottoes, fish, distant houses . . . all carved of shining stone by millions upon countless millions of water drops over centuries past number. He was so completely enthralled by the unearthly beauty of the place that he even forgot his predicament for a few moments.

And then he noticed that his flashlight was growing so weak that it no longer threw a clearly defined beam. It must have been getting weaker for some time, he thought, but his eyes had adjusted themselves to the failing light.

He looked at his watch, wondering that the flashlight batteries had run down so soon. The watch had run down, too, and had stopped. He couldn't remember. Had he wound it before coming to the cave? He was chilled now. It was cold and damp in the limestone passages. He shivered and pulled up his collar.

The panic rose up again. He didn't know how long he had been in the cave. Had it been only a short while, or so many hours that his watch had run down? He said to himself as calmly as he was able, "I'll have to get where I'm going before the light fails altogether."

He began to run.

The illusion grew that he was trying to overtake the end of the flashlight's beam. When he did catch up with it, that would be the end. He had completely forgotten the infrared light on the camera, even though the case banged against his side as he ran. He had been carrying it for so long it had become a part of him.

He dodged through passages, rounded turns, leaped over stalagmites. Once he had to crawl on his hands and knees under water-smooth limestone, pushing his rifle ahead of him.

And all the time he was catching up to the end of the light. The radius of illumination narrowed as the batteries failed, increasing the danger of stumbling into a sudden crevice. Outside, the flashlight would have been rejected long ago as a source of light. But far underground, with no other light of any kind, it was still useful.

Running more slowly now, at a stumbling dogtrot, he broke into a cave larger than any he had seen since the first one, at the end of the passage from the Black Buddha. The feeble light failed to reach the opposite wall.

Rick stopped, panting for breath. He knew he had to rest. He found a natural seat next to a twisted pillar of limestone and sat down.

The light slowly faded until there was only the dimmest of red tints to the bulb, and then that vanished too, and he was again in total darkness. As he watched the light fade, he remembered the infrared. Now he got the glasses from the case and put them on. He took the camera out and adjusted the handstrap so it could be carried like a satchel. But he didn't turn on the light just yet. The battery had to be conserved at all costs. Because . . .

He swallowed hard. Because when the battery for the infrared light ran down, there would be nothing but darkness. Darkness would mean feeling his way through the limestone tangle, and he realized fully that he would not get far before death claimed him in the form of a yawning canyon in the limestone rock. He had passed many of them.

He set his jaw. That was ten hours away, because the battery would last that long. Ten hours was a long time if used wisely.

He closed his eyes and leaned back, dead tired. He dozed off.

Rick was never sure what awakened him, because there was no noise. It may have been the light on eyes made sensitive by ultimate blackness. But could a single candle have that much effect?

The candle was carried by a man. A Tibetan. The candle was in a tin container, punched full of holes. That was to keep it from being blown out in case of a draft, although there was little or no draft in the caverns.

When Rick opened his eyes the man was walking straight across the floor of the big cave, noiseless as a cat in feet wrapped in quilted cloth. The miracle was that Rick didn't cry out on seeing another human.

He sat frozen, watching the man. Then, as the stranger reached the far side of the cave, Rick came to life. If he lost this man, who obviously knew his way around, he was finished! Working at top speed he untied his shoelaces and slipped off his shoes. Then, in stocking feet, he padded silently across the floor.

The candle was his guide. He didn't need the infrared beam yet. He would follow the candle, and if it led him right into the hands of the enemy, that was better than perishing alone of hunger in the blackness of the inner caves.

As he went, wary of a backward look by his quarry, he put his rifle under his arm and fumbled to tie a knot in his laces. It took time, since he was carrying the camera in one hand now. When he finally managed, he draped the shoes around his neck.

A dozen times he had been on the verge of abandoning the rifle as useless extra weight. Now he was glad he had held onto it.

Ahead, the candlelight bobbed and turned as the Tibetan, unaware that he was being followed, made his way through the caverns. Rick followed at a safe distance, close enough to avoid being left behind by a sudden turn.

There was a new feeling in the air suddenly, a feeling of space and of wetness. Rick sniffed. There was an odor, too, like decaying leaves, although much weaker. His hopes brightened. Was the Tibetan leading him out of the caves?

Then, so suddenly that he almost slipped from the edge, the path took him to a narrow ledge above a body of water of some kind.

The Tibetan was making his way along the ledge, candle held high in a search for something. When Rick switched on the infrared light for a moment, the incredible scene leaped to his eyes from the darkness. From under his feet a lake stretched away, its farther shore beyond the eight-hundred-yard range of the infrared light. He turned the light back and forth, seeking the end of the amazing body of water. But there was nothing except the shore on which he stood.

The water was dead calm. Not a ripple disturbed the glassy surface. He shot the invisible light straight down, and the water was so deep it looked black.

With a sudden start he realized he might lose the Tibetan candle bearer. He hurried after him, using the infrared light because the candle was too far away now to show him the path. With the glasses on, using the infrared light was just like using a powerful searchlight.

Far ahead, the candle stopped moving. Rick now proceeded more cautiously, and he switched off the infrared light in case the Tibetan should look back and possibly spy the glowing filament of the lamp.

The man was stooping over something, the candle resting on the stone next to him. Rick switched the light on, then off again. And he broke into a silent run. During the second the light had been on he had seen that the Tibetan was untying a boat!

He had an instant to make a decision. He reached a spot a few feet behind the preoccupied stranger, who was having trouble with the rope knot, and put the infrared camera down on the stone. Then, gripping the rifle firmly, he walked right up to the man.

"Hands up," he growled.

The Tibetan screamed.

He whirled, eyes wide with astonished fright, and he didn't even see the rifle. He swept an enormous knife from his belt and leaped!

Rick stumbled backward, and as he did, he realized that he couldn't shoot. He still needed the man for a guide. He swung the rifle, barrel first.

It was just as effective as it had been when he swung on Worthington Ko. The barrel connected with an audible *thunk*. The Tibetan fell forward on his face.

Frightened out of his wits, Rick rolled him over, pulled aside the sheepskin coat he wore and put his ear on the man's chest. Then he sighed with relief. He hadn't swung too hard. For a moment he had feared that the blow had killed the man. And that would have been almost as effective as holding the rifle barrel to his own head, because he still had no idea of where to go without the guide.

He debated for a moment, then lifted the Tibetan, dragged him to the boat and dumped him in. It was a flat-bottomed craft with blunt ends and primitive oarlocks. The oars were poles with round disks of wood on the ends.

He collected the candle and the camera, placed them on a thwart, and went to work on the rope. It was reeved through an iron ring that jutted from the stone. The sight gave him heart. Where there was iron, men came often. At least he was sure that held true in this case. But his victory had spurred him on and he didn't want to sit quietly and wait. He wanted to keep going.

He untied the knot, blew out the candle, shipped the oars and pushed off. Something was on the other side of this Lake of Darkness. He couldn't imagine what, but he intended to find out!

CHAPTER XVII

Through a Pair of Dark Glasses

SOMEWHERE, perhaps, beyond the Lake of Darkness, was Long Shadow.

Rick felt certain of it. The Tibetan who lay unconscious at his feet had been going somewhere. He had walked steadily and purposefully, with some definite destination in mind. What was more logical than to assume that the Tibetan had been heading for the hidden plant where heavy water was being produced?

Once the plant was found, Long Shadow would be found there, also. Even if he were not there at the moment, he would come. And when he did, Rick intended to do something about it. He had no definite plans. He only knew that somehow he would force Long Shadow to unlock the gate to the outer world.

His oars dipped rhythmically as he pulled out into the lake. The infrared light was directed toward a jutting edge of limestone on the shore he had just left.

He was using the rock formation as a marker so he could steer a straight course.

He wondered about his friends. Were they lost, too? Or had they managed to keep to the right trail by following the tiny drops of candle wax? The odd tin candleholder explained why there wasn't more wax to follow. The holder caught most, but not all of the drippings.

The rocky shore of the underground lake receded rapidly. Rick stopped rowing and turned, switching the infrared light toward the direction in which he was heading. He could see the opposite shore now, but dimly. Knowing that the infrared light was effective at eight hundred yards, he estimated the lake to be about twelve hundred yards wide. That was over three-fifths of a mile.

When he shot the light up and down the lake, he saw nothing but the black water. That meant the lake was more than sixteen hundred yards long. He turned the light upward and surveyed the ceiling. It was irregular, varying in height from a dozen feet to over two hundred. In one place, the ceiling came down to within a few feet of the black water.

It was an eerie place. Rick's quick imagination turned him into the mythical Charon, who ferried the dead across the River Styx into Hades. He grinned mirthlessly. The limp figure of the Tibetan gave substance to the picture.

He bent over the man, reaching for his wrist. The pulse was weak but steady. He had given the Tibetan a healthy belt. There was no sign of returning consciousness. But Rick wasn't worried. If he had hurt the man badly, the pulse would have been thready and unsteady. He would wake up presently, and his head would feel like a pillow stuffed with rocks, but otherwise he would be all right. Rick knew. He had been knocked out himself a couple of times.

He resumed rowing, and his steady strokes brought him closer to the opposite shore. He turned to examine it and saw that a rocky ledge rose gradually out of the water. In a short time he felt the boat grind against the limestone.

He got out and pulled the craft up on the shore, which was worn smooth by the water. The ledge varied from ten to fifty feet in width. Beyond it, the roof of the cavern came down sharply to form a curving wall broken in countless places. He could see into the broken places nearest him. They were the beginnings of more cave labyrinths.

Now that he had reached the opposite shore, what was he to do? Again he leaned over the Tibetan. The man showed no signs of returning consciousness.

Rick cast his invisible light up and down the shore. Nothing indicated that humans ever had been there before him. He realized that the wisest thing would be to wait until his guide returned to consciousness and then force him to lead the way once more. But he was impatient. Somewhere along the shore there must be signs he could follow.

He pulled the boat up as high as he could, then used

strips torn from the Tibetan's own clothes to bind and gag him. That done, he picked up the infrared camera and his rifle and stood a moment in indecision. Which way?

It was a tossup. Finally he decided to keep going in the general direction the Tibetan had led him. He paused long enough to inspect his rifle. After firing, he had failed to lever another cartridge into the chamber. He did so now, then put the hammer on half cock so it couldn't fire accidentally, and started off.

It was easy going in most places. But now and then he came to a point where the shore ledge narrowed and he had to crawl. Once he skirted an outcropping by walking in the water, feeling his way carefully so he wouldn't step off a ledge into the depths.

After a while he began to think he hadn't been very smart. He was getting exactly nowhere. As far ahead as the infrared beam could penetrate, there was nothing but the curving shore. In some places the lake narrowed to a channel less than a hundred feet wide, then it broadened again until he could no longer see the opposite shore. He couldn't guess how far he had walked from the boat. He thought it must be at least a quarter mile.

Presently he found a place where a limestone pillar made a comfortable back rest and sat down. He switched off the infrared light, and instantly all light was blotted out. It was startling, even more so than when he had switched off the flashlight, because the infrared beam gave the illusion of a sort of gray daylight.

He sat quietly, waiting for some of the weariness to leave his legs, his eyes closed. After a while he opened them again, more from habit than with the intention of seeing anything. He couldn't see even the tip of his nose it was so dark. Then suddenly he realized it wasn't as dark as he had expected!

There was a faint luminous quality that outlined the shore of the lake. He studied the line of demarkation, then guessed that the faint luminosity must come from microscopic plant or animal life that clung to the rock underwater. Sea water had a phosphorescence sometimes for the same reason.

His eyes followed the faint line up the shore in the direction he had been traveling. The silver phosphorescence turned a faint yellow. Almost out of the range of his vision the yellow was picked up by the water, like the dimmest moonlight.

He studied it for long minutes, trying to figure out the reason for the phenomenon, then he almost leaped out of his skin. The water was reflecting the yellow light! It didn't come from the water the way the luminous silver did!

He got to his feet. Reflection meant man-made light!

It was hard to follow the faint yellow light. When he switched on the infrared, the light vanished completely. When the infrared was off, he couldn't find his way.

He compromised, going a hundred feet or so with the infrared on, then turning it off and sitting quietly until his eyes adjusted themselves and he could see the yellow glow once more. After he did this a few times he could see that the light was growing slightly stronger.

Then, as he progressed, he realized why he couldn't see the source of the light. It was around a corner of the rock wall.

After several minutes of alternate walking and waiting he reached the corner. It dropped sharply into the water, and when he flashed the infrared down, he saw that the water was black. No shelf here to walk on. He debated for a moment. He could swim around, or he could try to find another way. There were plenty of cave openings. One of them might go through.

He had been lost once, and he didn't intend to let that happen again. He tore open the packet of emergency rations he had brought, searching for something with which to lay a trail.

Inside the waxed container were little cans of food and a packet of hard crackers. The crackers would do.

But looking at the food reminded him that he hadn't eaten in a long time. He didn't know if it was hours, or days. He had lost all track of time. He took the can key and unwound the narrow sealing strip on a container of cheese. It tasted wonderful. He devoured every bit of it, including the crumbs left in the can. Then he opened a can of meat and ate that, too. He had been sipping at his canteen at various times, but it was still more than half full. He detached the canteen cup and filled it from the lake, tasting it cautiously. The water had a flat taste, like boiled water, but it was all right. He drank deeply, then filled the canteen.

His hunger and thirst satisfied, he surveyed the various openings around him, then chose the one nearest the corner he wished to get around. At the very entrance, he placed the empty cheese tin. Inside the cave, he turned to be sure it was clearly visible, then walked across to an opening that seemed likely to lead him in the right direction. He placed the second can at that opening and went into the passage formed by a series of stalagmite columns. It was a dead end. He returned to the cave where he had left the cans, picked up the empty meat can, and tried another entry.

He was completely calm now. He knew that humans, even though enemies, were not far away. And he was quite sure that his friends were all right. They would take steps to leave a trail so they would not get lost as he had done.

The second passage was better. He wound in and out through the limestone formations, leaving a trail of broken cracker crumbs. Every now and then he turned to see that the trail was plain. He grinned. Hadn't he read a story when he was a kid about some children who had left a trail of crumbs only to have the birds eat them?

No danger of that here. No self-respecting bird would get near the place.

It wasn't long before he ran out of crumbs. Then he tore his handkerchief into tiny bits and used that. When he reached the end of the cloth scraps, he sat down to rest, turning off the infrared light while he carefully shredded a big piece of his shirttail.

As his eyes adjusted themselves to the darkness, he

saw the yellow light again, only stronger this time! Carefully, his heart beating excitedly, he turned the infrared light in the direction of the yellow glow and switched it on. Before him was a big opening in the limestone. He surveyed the floor carefully and saw that there was nothing over which to trip. He turned off the infrared light, and, leaving a trail of torn cloth behind him, he crawled toward the source of the light.

He came out on the shore of the lake once more. Before him stretched the black water, the yellow light dancing across its surface. And the source of the light was not from candles, but from torches!

Across the water, perhaps a hundred yards away, a half dozen torches burned, their light lost in the emptiness of the great lake cave. Near the torches he could see figures moving and knew with sudden relief that he had found the enemy camp.

He turned on the infrared light, aiming it at the torches, and through his special glasses he saw the scene light up.

Where the torches blazed was a great shelf of rock, stretching back several hundred feet to where the rock wall began once more. On the shelf were a dozen men, sitting around a tiny cooking fire much paler than the torches themselves. They were Tibetans, like the one he had captured.

He saw an odd structure at the water line and after a little study realized that it was a barge of some kind, perhaps a floating pier. It had odd derricklike wooden ladders on it. There were four of them, perhaps three feet high. Beyond the barge he made out at least two flat-bottomed boats.

Further back, against the limestone wall, he could see tents or lean-tos made of some kind of cloth. He couldn't see clearly, but thought the cloth might be felt. This, then, was a permanent camp! The tents must be there to offer some protection against the cold and dampness.

He inspected the men again. They were all short. None of them could be Long Shadow.

"Now what?" Rick asked himself.

It was certain that Long Shadow would come to the camp sooner or later. It was almost as certain that Scotty, Zircon, and Chahda, if they followed the trail of the wax candles carefully, would arrive sooner or later at the boat landing to which the Tibetan had led him. Always provided they hadn't been ambushed. He shivered at the thought. The cave formations would make it easy for the enemy to lie in wait. Then, even with their old-fashioned muskets and lack of shooting ability, they could pick off the little party.

But they wouldn't do it without cost! Scotty was deadly with a rifle. Zircon was a better than average shot.

Rick debated. It was no good to make his presence known. Far better to lie in wait until Long Shadow came. Then, if he could take the camp by surprise, his rifle would do the rest for him.

But how to take it by surprise?

He scanned the shore around the camp. In several

places between him and the camp shelf, the rock wall came right down to the lake's edge. Unless he wanted to search for a way through the caves, he would have to swim. Or use a boat.

Beyond the last sheer place, the camp shelf started. Its edge curved and twisted for a little distance. If he could get to the starting point, he could keep undercover easily enough. Then, making his way along the wall, he could probably escape being seen until he was almost at the tents. With luck, a sudden dash would bring him right to the enemy without being seen first.

That was how he would do it. He would go back and get the boat, then lie in wait in this very place until the time came. He withdrew from the entrance, then paused suddenly. The men around the fire were getting to their feet and walking toward the water. He watched as they peered into the darkness in the direction he thought of as "down lake." One of them ran to a torch, pulled it out of its holder, ran back to the water's edge, and waved it.

A signal! To whom?

Two of the men were kneeling just beyond the barge, and a moment later they proceeded to get into the two flat-bottomed boats he had seen. What they had been doing was untying the boats. He watched as they rowed out onto the black lake.

They must be going after someone!

Rick hurried back the way he had come, following the path of torn cloth, then the broken cracker crumbs. He would have to hurry. The Tibetans might have gone after Long Shadow!

He retraced his steps at a pace that was half-walking, half-running. The trail he had left showed clearly in the infrared light. In a few moments he came out of the caves onto the lake shore once more, and he saw the signal that had summoned the boats. A red light was now clearly visible. He thought it was right at the point from which he had pushed off in the Tibetan's boat.

A sudden thought struck him. Wouldn't they miss the Tibetan and the boat? He hurried faster. Now and then he stopped to listen, and he could hear the sound of oars in the water.

It didn't take long to reach his boat. When he leaned over the Tibetan, frightened black eyes peered up at him. He tested the man's bonds. They were tight enough to be effective, but not so tight they cut off his circulation. He knew the gag was uncomfortable, but he didn't dare remove it. As assurance that he meant no harm, he patted the man on the shoulder. Some of the wild fright went out of the beady eyes.

Working quietly, Rick pushed the boat out into the water. He wasn't afraid of being seen. Candles or torches didn't cast enough light to penetrate the blackness as the infrared beam did. But he might be heard. He had to be as quiet as possible.

He used only one oar, kneeling in the stern and paddling the flat-bottomed craft like a canoe. The infrared camera, placed on the seat with the beam directed ahead of him, gave him plenty of light to see. Once in a while he turned the beam around. The two boats were making good progress toward the red signal. The beam of the infrared camera didn't penetrate far enough for him to see what or who was under the red light.

He rounded the corner that had blocked his way and paddled silently along the rocky wall. The two boats were out of sight now.

Rounding the corner gave him a clear view of the torches, but he knew the men around them couldn't see him.

The way was longer than he had thought. He paddled in and out of coves, past grottoes in the rocky wall. Then, at last, he saw the little pile of torn cloth he had left on the shore at the end of his cave trail. He had put all the cloth not needed for marking trail in one place, not because he had been foresighted, but because he hadn't needed it any more. He was glad now of the accident that marked the right place, otherwise he couldn't have identified it from the rest of the openings in the wall.

He pulled the boat up to it and anchored it by the rope to a convenient stalagmite. Then he half-lifted, half-dragged the trussed Tibetan into the cave and out of sight of the lake.

Rick searched the water for some sign of the boats, and thought he heard them coming. He went back to the Tibetan, took his canteen, unscrewed the top, and placed it on the rock. Then, kneeling over his captive, he took the man's throat in one hand. With the other he undid the rag that held the gag in place. Pressure of his fingers warned the Tibetan he would be strangled if he so much as squeaked. Then Rick pulled the torn rags he had used as a gag from the man's mouth, lifted him to a sitting position, and held the canteen to his lips with his free hand.

The Tibetan drank greedily. Rick let him rest for a moment, then held the canteen again. The man drank his fill, then nodded his thanks. Rick quickly replaced the gag and bound it in place, then used another piece of cloth torn from the man's clothing to lash one leg to a stalagmite. He didn't want to risk having the man wriggle to the entrance at the wrong time, and sound an alarm.

Rick was exultant. High excitement was rising in him, because he thought it was only a matter of time now before Long Shadow would come, even if his enemy was not already in one of the boats that were making their way back to the camp.

He switched out the infrared light, placing the camera on the ground, pointing toward the boat landing. Then he lay down on his stomach, rifle thrust out in front of him and handy to his hand. He could wait. He could wait days, if necessary. Because once Long Shadow came, he would force him to show the way to the outside, and he would force him to locate the others.

If Long Shadow refused to co-operate . . . Rick's lips tightened. Then at least he wouldn't be lonesome in the Caves of Fear. His enemy would be his company until the end.

CHAPTER XVIII

The Hostages

A FAINT splashing warned Rick that the boats were approaching. In a few moments they were opposite his position. He swung the infrared light around toward them and snapped it on.

There were two men in the lead boat, one rowing and the other taking his ease in the stern. Rick's heart leaped as he saw that the passenger was of very slender build. Was it Long Shadow? He couldn't see his face clearly. He looked at the second boat, and a sudden grin split his lips.

Worthington Ko!

The Chinese merchant was sitting at ease, and there was no mistaking his portly figure. Besides, he twisted on the wooden seat, making himself more comfortable, and for an instant his face was toward Rick.

"Good," Rick muttered to himself. If the slender man wasn't Long Shadow, at least he would have Ko to deal with. The Chinese with the glass eye could, he knew, speak English, although it was probable that Long Shadow could, too.

He watched as the boats reached the barge. Ko and the slender man got out. Rick studied the stranger, noting that he was taller than Ko, and so thin that, compared with the portly merchant, he looked like an animated bean pole.

"He surely must be Long Shadow," Rick told himself. As soon as the excitement of their arrival had died down among the Tibetans, he intended to get into his boat and start toward the camp.

Ko and the stranger talked together for a moment, then the latter gestured toward the Tibetans. The Tibetans ran toward the tents while the two newcomers waited.

Rick watched the Tibetans, his brow furrowed. Surely they weren't going to strike camp! He revised his plans hastily. If they did start to take down the tents, he would dump his prisoner back in the boat. Then he would follow wherever they went.

The Tibetans vanished into the tents, and in a moment they came out again.

And they were leading Scotty, Zircon, and Chahda! Rick gasped.

His friends had been in the camp all the time, prisoners! He groaned softly. If he had only known, he might have gotten to them while the boats were gone and the number of guards was temporarily reduced. He got to his knees, determined to start for them right away. Then he paused as his three friends were led before the two strangers. They were all erect, their hands tied behind them.

Anyway, prisoners or not, they were evidently none the worse for their captivity. Again he started for the boat, and again he paused. What if Long Shadow and Ko intended loading them in the boats? It might be wiser to wait. He sank down to a sitting position, caressing the cold metal of his rifle. The next few moments would tell the story.

Worthington Ko stepped forward, confronting Zircon. The Chinese nodded his head, then deliberately slapped the scientist across the face.

Zircon couldn't strike back. But his legs were free. One massive leg swung in a giant punt that caught the Chinese squarely in the stomach. Worthington Ko flew backward like a rag doll and slid along the limestone floor. Rick watched the tableau, spellbound.

The Tibetans ran forward.

Rick put the camera down, light pointing at the group across the way. Then he raised his rifle and sighted in. He'd get some of them before they could harm his friends. His finger tightened slowly on the trigger.

And then the Tibetans fell back as Long Shadow barked an order.

Worthington Ko got to his feet, bent over, both hands on his stomach. He weaved a little. The breath had been knocked right out of him, Rick thought.

The Tibetans and Long Shadow watched as Ko

straightened up, very slowly. He ran his hands gingerly over his big stomach. Then, walking unsteadily, he moved back to within a few feet of Zircon. He called out something and one of the Tibetans ran forward.

Rick's throat clogged as the torchlight reflected from a shiny blade. Ko took the blade and swished it through the air. Then, drawing it back, he stepped forward.

The Chinese was squarely in Rick's sights. He squeezed the trigger and the rifle recoiled against his shoulder. The shot thundered through the echoing cave.

Ko staggered. He dropped the blade, took a couple of hesitant steps backward, and then sat down hard.

There was sudden chaos in the camp across the way. The Tibetans ran back and forth aimlessly like sheep. Long Shadow bellowed orders. Then he ran to a torch, pulled it out of the socket, and heaved it into the water. The Tibetans got the idea. The torches flashed through the air and then hissed out in the water.

Long Shadow felt his way toward the three Spindrifters, calling out orders to the Tibetans. Rick suddenly realized that, of all in sight, only he could see! Long Shadow and his men thought they were safe in the darkness.

He watched, rifle at his shoulder, as Long Shadow collected the Tibetans. Then he realized that the enemy intended herding Scotty, Zircon, and Chahda into the caves. Probably they were certain that in the caves they would be safe from whoever had fired from the darkness.

Ko was still sitting. He had one hand pressed to his side.

The Tibetans were groping for their prisoners. Rick grinned. He aimed at the stone under their feet and fired. There was a chorus of yells. He levered another cartridge into the chamber and fired again.

The Tibetans fled, charging blindly toward the cave openings beyond the tents.

Long Shadow kept yelling orders, groping around in the blackness, but the Tibetans paid no attention. They reached the back wall of the cave. Two of them went headlong into openings. Others crashed into the walls, fell, crawled sideways, scrambling until they found the openings they so frantically sought.

Long Shadow's voice could be heard screaming in fury for his men to come back.

He couldn't see, as Rick could, that they were all now in the caves behind their leader.

Finally, giving up, Long Shadow started for safety himself.

It would never do to allow the thin man to get away, Rick thought. He wanted Long Shadow. He and his companions had questions to ask him, and they needed him to get them out of the Caves of Fear. He sighted carefully at the long legs that were feeling their way toward the back wall. He fired.

Long Shadow stumbled headlong, then he started to crawl. Rick stood up and yelled. "Gang! Get Long Shadow!"

His words echoed eerily through the cave.

Zircon understood and bellowed. "Where is he?"

Rick thought quickly. The three were still standing in a line. He shouted orders.

"Right face. Forward march!"

Like a well-trained machine, his friends obeyed. They marched forward steadily. But they were slightly off. He remembered the correct command.

"Left oblique! March!"

Scotty swung a quarter left, bumped into Zircon. Chahda stood still, not understanding. Neither had Zircon comprehended the command. Rick yelled, "Scotty! Turn right just a fraction."

Scotty did so. "Now," Rick called. "He's about ten feet in front of you."

Scotty moved forward, feeling his way a step at a time. When he was almost on Long Shadow, Rick yelled, "You're there!"

Long Shadow turned over on his back and clawed in his pockets.

"Watch out!" Rick screamed. "He's got a gun!"

Scotty jumped, feet first. He missed Long Shadow by a fraction, landing next to his chest.

"Fall to the left!" Rick yelled.

Scotty crashed down across the man, calling to Zircon and Chahda. Guided by their friend's voice, the two reached his side quickly. Rick couldn't hear what Scotty said, but the big scientist suddenly sat down, his back to Long Shadow. A moment later he writhed away, and he had the pistol between his bound hands.

Rick sighed his relief. "Wait!" he yelled. "I'll be right there!"

He didn't dare take his eyes off the scene long

enough to pick up his prisoner. Time enough for that later. He untied the boat and got in. He knelt, placing the rifle on the seat in front of him next to the infrared camera. Then, using the oar as a paddle once more, he started straight across to the camp.

It wasn't a far journey. But as he reached the halfway mark, two of the Tibetans looked cautiously out of their hiding place. Rick put the oar across the gunwales, picked up his rifle, and sighted carefully. Fortunately, there wasn't so much as a ripple on the water. The boat was perfectly steady.

He squeezed the trigger, and the stalactite directly over their heads shattered into a thousand pieces, showering them with limestone. They didn't wait for a second shot. He could hear their yells even after they had ducked back into the caves. They weren't used to sharpshooting in total darkness.

Rick smiled as he resumed paddling. He could understand how they felt. He wasn't used to it, either.

In a few moments he was at the barge. He tied the boat to one of the odd derrick affairs and scrambled out. Then, picking up the camera and rifle, he hurried to his friends.

Scotty and Chahda were using Long Shadow as a bench. Zircon sat a little distance apart, trying to peer toward Rick through the darkness.

"Dark in here, isn't it?" Rick inquired pleasantly.

"Rick! You old muttonhead!" Scotty exclaimed.

"Thank God you're safe," Zircon said.

Chahda grinned the widest grin ever and said, "Also

giving much thanks that friend Rick has eyes like cat which see in dark!" The Hindu boy didn't know about the infrared camera, unless the others had explained it to him. There hadn't been time back at camp, and Rick hadn't thought of it, anyway.

In a moment the three were untied, rubbing circulation back into their wrists.

"Let's get a light!" Zircon said. "I think we had better see to the wounded. I assume there are wounded? I know Ko was hit. And just as he was about to carve my head from my shoulders, too."

"He's sitting over there," Rick said.

"Where's there?" Scotty asked.

He kept forgetting that only he could see. "Where he dropped. Long Shadow is hit, too. I don't know how badly."

For the first time, they heard their enemy's voice. It was rather high, but cultured and pleasant. "Not badly. Although I believe my ankle may be broken. I have felt, and I don't believe I am bleeding much."

Rick knelt quickly and put the infrared light on the wound. Long Shadow was right. It hadn't bled much, and Zircon, looking the wound over after borrowing the glasses, told him, "I doubt that the ankle is broken. The wound is clean."

"Stay where you are," Rick warned him. "We'll bandage you after we look at Ko."

"I have no intention of going anywhere," Long Shadow said. "Not when some magic I don't understand permits you to see in complete darkness."

Rick took the glasses from Zircon's hand. In the interval during which the scientist was wearing them, he had understood how the others felt. The darkness was absolute. He put the glasses on again and walked over to Ko, talking so his friends could follow the sound of his voice.

"Well, Mr. Ko," he said, "you got a little surprise, didn't you?"

The Chinese with the glass eye groaned. "You have won," he complained weakly. "Now have the kindness to let me go to my ancestors in peace."

"Better let me take a look at him," Zircon said.

Rick walked to the scientist's side and took one of his hands. Then he took off the glasses and pressed them into the hand he was holding. That done, he stood in the blackness and waited.

"Lie flat," presently Zircon said.

"Please go away," Ko groaned.

"Lie flat," Zircon ordered.

There was the sound of ripping cloth. Zircon grunted. "Hmmmm."

Ko moaned. "I wish to go to my ancestors alone."

"You're not going to your ancestors," Zircon replied scornfully. "I doubt that they'd have you. In case you're interested, Rick's bullet merely plowed a nice, round hole through some of the fat on your right side. You haven't even lost enough blood to make the wound interesting."

Ko's voice was suddenly animated. "Are you sure?"

"Quite sure. No, don't try to get up. Stay where you

are. If you try to run I'll order our seeing-eye marksman to finish the job." Zircon continued, "Rick, Scotty, Chahda. Stay where you are. I saw some torches stacked in one of the tents. I'll get them and be right back."

The three boys assured him that they wouldn't move. Rick, for one, had no intention of prowling about in the blackness.

While they waited, Scotty asked, "What happened to you, Rick?"

Rick hesitated. He couldn't give an adequate account of what he had experienced during the recent hours. Or was it weeks? He summed it up. "After we got separated, I couldn't find you again. I wandered around. Then I sat down in a big cave and fell asleep. When I woke, there was a Tibetan with a candle. I followed him to a boat landing, slugged him, and rowed across the lake. He's waiting, tied up, across the lake at the spot from where I fired. How about you?"

"We look for you," Chahda said. "We look a long time, and almost get lost ourself."

"Finally we decided we'd better push on and find Long Shadow," Scotty continued. "We tracked the drippings from the candles for hours. It was slow work. Then, while we were resting, we got jumped from behind. They didn't even have to bother about lights, because one of our flashlights was on, and it was getting so weak we couldn't see more than ten feet. They came out of the darkness with a rush and there we were. They made us walk to the boat landing, called the boats from here, and brought us over. We've been sitting in one of those tents for hours. You know the rest."

How rapidly they could cover the tortured hours of travel in a few words, Rick thought. But he said only, "I'm glad we're all together again."

"How you see in dark?" Chahda asked.

Rick explained briefly. The Hindu boy chuckled. "Plenty mystery for one who not know, you bet! I scared myself, like the men who ran."

Then Zircon came back. He brought out matches and in a moment torches were blazing again. They bandaged the two enemies as best they could, using clean handkerchiefs which Chahda and Scotty carried. And Rick got his first good look at Long Shadow's face.

The man was incredibly thin. His skin was stretched over the bones of his face like parchment, and it had a sallow ivory tinge even in the ruddy torchlight. His eyes were black, with just the faintest hint of a Mongoloid fold.

"Are you a Eurasian?" Rick asked bluntly.

"Yes." Long Shadow smiled. "I'm one quarter Burmese. The other three-quarters doesn't matter."

"You know our names," Rick said. "I'm sure you do. But we don't know yours."

Long Shadow laughed. "You could never pronounce my Burmese name and the other name I use is of no importance."

Zircon and the others had been listening. Now the scientist said, "We'll have plenty of chance to talk, Rick. At the moment I'm concerned with getting out of here. After a bit of exploration of course. It's almost certain that the heavy water comes from here. Although I don't know the source."

Scotty motioned toward the Lake of Darkness. "Bradley said to bring a Nansen bottle and a rubber boat. He must have known about this. Why would he say to bring a Nansen bottle if not to take a sample from the lake?"

Zircon flashed a look at Long Shadow. The Eurasian smiled gently. "That's a good question Mr. Scott asked," he told them. "But don't look to me for the answer."

"Search the tents," Zircon ordered. "Chahda, keep an eye on our two friends."

The three Americans walked to the felt tents and began searching through them. Zircon used the infrared camera. Rick and Scotty took torches.

Rick was feeling through a pile of furs when Zircon called, "Here are the flashlights!"

Zircon's had run down, but Scotty's, and Chahda's big lights were still useful. They made the search much easier. Rick went back to the pile of skins and found that they were plastic-lined water bags, similar to the ones they had found on the way to Korse Lenken. Then, stacked in a corner of the tent, he found some Nansen bottles!

At the same moment, Scotty called from the next tent. "Look what I found!"

He had located the ammunition supply. There was powder and ball for the old muskets the Tibetans used, two boxes of machine pistol cartridges, and a small case of grenades!

"Now we know where Ko got the one he tried to use

on us," Rick said. "But where did they come from in the first place?"

"The war," Scotty guessed. "There must be tons of ammo and ordnance of all kinds floating around China. What makes me wonder is why the Tibetans don't have modern rifles."

"I suspect the answer is their natural conservatism," Zircon suggested. "They are slow to change. And such guns as they use are handed down from father to son. I don't doubt that modern rifles were offered them and that they refused."

Rick knew something of the Oriental mind, although not much, and he realized that Zircon was probably right. In a land of ancestor worship, change was resisted.

Scotty stuffed grenades in each pocket. "Just in case we get into a fight on the way out," he explained.

Rick was glad to leave the deadly things to his friend. Scotty knew about grenades from his tour of duty in the Marines; he had thrown more than a few himself.

"Nansen bottles in the next tent, professor," Rick said. "There must be something to this business of getting stuff out of the lake. But golly, you don't get heavy water out of natural water, do you?"

"I don't know," Zircon said. "There is only one precedent I can think of. Have you ever heard of Lake Baikal?"

Neither boy had.

"It's a very large lake in Siberia, just above Mongolia," the scientist told them. "It is also very deep. A few years ago, before the Iron Curtain closed down, word came out of Russia that some scientists had succeeded in getting heavy water samples out of Baikal. That is the only precedent that I know.

"It is true," he continued, "that heavy water has a tendency to sink. Naturally enough, since it is heavier. But for enough to form on the bottom of a body of water, there would have to be great depth and complete calm. Any current would stir the water up and the heavy water would merge with the normal once more."

"In other words, you need a lake like this one," Rick concluded.

"I must admit it fits the requirements," Zircon agreed. "And we've seen no sign of an industrial plant. These caverns certainly would be no place for one."

"We can soon tell," Scotty suggested. "Let's take a sample. When we get out, you can test it."

"Quite right," Zircon said. "And let's be quick about it."

It didn't take long to discover the reason for the odd little derricks on the barge. Each was equipped with a pulley and a reel of wire. Obviously, it was from here that the Nansen bottles were lowered.

While Chahda and Scotty remained on shore, Zircon and Rick pushed the barge out into the lake. Rick got a Nansen bottle ready.

The bottle was made of metal, each end equipped with a spring cap. The bottle was lowered on a wire with the ends open, permitting water to flow through it freely. When it reached the desired depth, a metal weight called a "messenger" was attached to the wire and dropped. The weight of the messenger released devices that closed the caps, thus trapping the water sample inside. A brass spigot on the side permitted the sample to be taken out easily when the bottle was hauled up again.

They had brought four bottles from Long Shadow's stores. The first one was lowered to the very bottom, and it took a long time getting there. The reel of wire with which the barge was equipped ran out and out until a full seven hundred feet of it had disappeared into the dark depths of the lake. Rick was glad the reel of wire had a geared handle. Pulling that weight up would be no fun.

Once the slackening of the wire told them that bottom had been reached, Zircon put the messenger on the wire and let it go. Seconds later, a tug on the wire told them it had struck and Rick reeled in.

Other samples were taken at five, ten, and fifteen feet from the bottom. Zircon marked the bottles, then they paddled back to shore.

Long Shadow spoke up. "Of course you have testing equipment?"

"At our camp near Korse Lenken," Zircon assured him.

"You'll find what you expect," the Eurasian said.

"Thank you. And now, we'll also thank you to lead us out of here."

"No," Long Shadow said.

"You're beaten," Zircon said reasonably. "Why not admit it and co-operate? We've nothing against you even if there were law in Tibet. See us to the outside and open the barred gate and you're at liberty to go."

Rick started to protest, then he realized Zircon was right. Law in this part of the world was the law of the rifle. There was nothing they could do to Long Shadow or Ko.

Long Shadow considered. "I suppose you're right. My little business deal is over, at least for the time being." He raised his voice and yelled in Tibetan.

The boys grabbed up their rifles as Tibetan heads showed from the caves, black eyes blinking in fear.

"They will carry me and Ko," Long Shadow said calmly. "Now let us be on our way." He smiled. "I must admit I have a selfish interest in all this worry about getting to the outside. This ankle is beginning to hurt, and I won't mind having one of the lamas with medical skill take a look at it."

"How about letting a Hong Kong police doctor take a look at it?" Rick asked. Long Shadow's cheerfulness was getting on his nerves. The man acted more like a guest than a prisoner.

"I don't think we need go that far," Long Shadow replied. "The lamas are quite capable."

"I wasn't concerned about your ankle," Rick corrected. "I was thinking that the Hong Kong police might like to get their hands on the kind of citizen who goes around shooting up hotels with a Schmeisser machine pistol."

Long Shadow stopped smiling abruptly. "You couldn't prove that," he said swiftly.

"Why not?" Scotty asked. "We'll let the police see if the slugs from your machine pistol don't match those in the hotel wall. By the way, where is the Schmeisser? I haven't seen it around."

Long Shadow recovered his grin. "You'll never see it again. I took the precaution of disposing of it, in case the police in the hotel area had been alerted. Don't bother to ask me how I got rid of it."

"We won't," Zircon replied. "Obviously, you wouldn't tell us. However, perhaps you will tell us how long it will take to get out of here?"

"About ten minutes."

At their evident surprise, Long Shadow added, "I should have said once we cross the lake it will take about ten minutes. You came a very long way around, you see. I realize you followed the candle droppings, but I'm afraid those were left some time ago, when I first explored the cave. The first entrance you tried was the correct one, even though you didn't suspect the presence of a door. When you took the open way, you approached by a very twisting path."

"Just to satisfy my curiosity," Scotty asked, "why did your men capture us, then bundle us into the boats and bring us here? And where were you all that time?"

Long Shadow shrugged. "I knew your guide and bearers were outside, at Korse Lenken, of course. My men have kept an eye on you. I also felt they probably would start a search after you failed to return. It was almost certain they would find the entrance to the caverns behind the Black Buddha, and, like you, they would probably follow the candle drippings. The drippings would lead them nowhere. Unless they found the secret door, there would be no chance of them finding you here in our permanent camp. Hence, I had you brought here. Ko and I were waiting in the cave I use for an office. When we thought time enough had elapsed for my orders to be carried out, we came here. Meanwhile, we took a nap. Are you satisfied?"

"You never intended that we should see daylight again," Rick stated. He winked at his friends. "Suppose we tie a few stalactites to your feet, and Ko's, and see how long it takes for you to get down to where the heavy water is?" He looked meaningly at the lake.

Ko groaned, but Long Shadow only smiled. "If that's the way you want it," he said, "it will at least be quick. Both of us are done for, whether you know it or not. Your Mr. Bradley will see to that."

As Long Shadow had said, it was little more than ten minutes after crossing the lake before the party reached the cave under the Black Buddha. They had passed through the cave where Rick had found the Tibetan. Again he realized how lucky he had been. Some good angel had led him to the main route. Had he fallen asleep in some other cave, he might still be wandering through the labyrinth.

The rifles taken from Scotty and Zircon by Long Shadow's men had been found in one of the tents. With

Rick's rifle, they were insurance against treachery. But Long Shadow seemed resigned, for some reason Rick couldn't fathom, and Ko did nothing but curse the bearers who carried him.

Before reaching the great cave they stopped at a blank wall. At a signal from Long Shadow, one of the Tibetans reached behind a stalagmite and pulled a lever. A section of the wall swung open, disclosing the passage they had thought stopped in a dead end.

In a few moments they were crossing the outer cave, and Rick saw at once that the bars across the entrance passage were gone.

"When the inner door opens from the inside, the bars also open," Long Shadow said. "There is another cave under this one where the mechanism is located. No, I am not responsible. The ancient ones who made the Black Buddha also made the doors and the mechanism."

Rick ran ahead through the passage. He found the leather thong that controlled the door and pulled. The metal tongue came out of its slot permitting the counterbalance to swing the trap door upward. The others were behind him with their lights, and Rick saw his shadow loom large on the wall behind the Black Buddha. In the same way, the Long Shadow had been projected upward, probably by the light from a candle in the hands of a Tibetan bearer. He experimented, backing down a few steps. His shadow seemed to fold downward into the oblong box of light cast by the flashlights. When he walked up the stairs again, the shadow grew out of the bottom of the projected oblong of light.

As Rick reached floor level, he froze suddenly, his finger slipping the hammer of his rifle to full cock. There were lights in the cave! As he turned to call a warning, yellow-robed lamas, who had seen the reflected light on the rear wall, poured around the statue with wild yells, their torches held high.

"Something's up," Rick called to the others. "Watch it!"

Under the threat of Rick's rifle, then Scotty's and Zircon's, the lamas fell back until the group stood alongside the Black Buddha, looking into the cave. There were torches everywhere! And cooking fires. Rick's first thought was that they had returned in the midst of a religious celebration.

And then he saw Sing. The Chinese guide ran to them, his face split by a wide grin.

"You came," he exclaimed happily. "We were about to tear the mountain down, stone by stone! Where is the Indian boy?"

Chahda came from behind the statue, herding the Tibetans who carried Long Shadow, Ko, and the Nansen bottles. Sing turned and yelled.

The lamas broke into cries of approval at the sight of Chahda. Several of them ran to him and pressed his hand. He was a favorite, obviously.

"They came to help when I told them the Indian boy was in danger," Sing explained. "We were ready to start digging holes to find the caverns, because we couldn't find the door." He eyed Long Shadow curiously and grinned at the sight of Ko. "Should I get my frying pan again?" he asked.

"Might be a good idea," Rick said.

"My boss not come yet?" Chahda asked.

Sing clapped hands to his head in a gesture of self-annoyance. "I forgot. A letter came. One of the consulate guards, a Chinese who knows this part of the world, brought it from Chungking. It may be from Mr. Bradley, because it came originally from Hong Kong."

Zircon took the envelope while Rick, Scotty, and Chahda looked over his shoulder. The envelope was marked for delivery from Hong Kong to Chungking via diplomatic pouch. It was addressed to Zircon, with the note, "Urgent. Forward by messenger." Bradley's initials were signed to it.

The scientist ripped the envelope open and, looking around to be sure Long Shadow and Ko were out of earshot, he read:

" 'Have all the answers except the source. When you find it, destroy it if possible. If you get Long Shadow or Worthington Ko, don't bother bringing them back to Hong Kong, if they're still alive. Leave them at Korse Lenken. Cable me from Chungking when you return.' "

It was signed "Bradley."

"I like his confidence in us," Zircon remarked. "Not 'if,' but 'when.' "

"My boss does not know what it means to fail," Chahda said.

"I can see one failure," Zircon remarked. "How does one destroy a body of water?"

Scotty's forehead wrinkled thoughtfully. "Couldn't

we stir it up? The heavy water is all at the bottom. If we could give it a stir, the heavy stuff would mix with the rest."

"But would maybe settle right back," Chahda objected.

"Not for a few thousand years," Zircon said. "A good idea, Scotty. Do you happen to have a spoon seven hundred feet long?"

Scotty grinned. "Yes. Mr. Ko supplied one." He reached into his pocket and pulled out a grenade. "These will do the best job of stirring that black cup of tea that you've ever seen."

"Capital!" Zircon exclaimed. "They'll do perfectly, Scotty." He looked at the boys. "Who wants to go back?"

Sing spoke up. "I will go, and some of the lamas should, too. The monastery should know all about these caves, in case something like this ever happens again." He spoke to the lamas in Tibetan. They consulted briefly, then nodded assent. Five of them stepped forward.

"And Scotty and I will go," Rick volunteered. "I want to see how this spoon works." He looked at Long Shadow and Ko. "Maybe they ought to go back and see the end of their racket, whatever it is."

"No need," Zircon said. "They know it's the end, and Bradley does too. Which is more than we know, I must say. But we'll find out from Bradley very soon."

Rick hefted his rifle. "Incidentally, there's one thing I want to do before we go back."

"And that is?"

He grinned at the scientist. "I want to go hunting blue sheep."

"Me, too," Scotty chimed in.

Zircon chuckled. "Very well. One day for sheep before we hit the trail. Since Bradley prohibits our taking revenge on the enemy, we'll take it out on the local livestock. Now get going. And do a thorough job."

CHAPTER XIX

Canton Charlie's

"You've come a long way, lads," Keaton-Yeats said. "From golden mice to blue sheep and back to golden mice again. I must say, you should be thoroughly familiar with the animal kingdom by now."

"They very familiar with animal world," Chahda agreed. "Also, sometimes become part of that world by making jackasses of their selves. Like when shooting blue sheep."

The boys had each bagged a blue sheep, but at considerable risk to life and limb. In the process, they had gotten themselves marooned on a rock ledge high above Korse Lenken, from which Sing, with the help of the bearers, had managed to rescue them.

"Never mind," Carl Bradley said. "They got their sheep, even if it almost took their necks to do it. Those heads will make nice trophies by the time the taxidermist is through with them."

The heads were in a Hong Kong shop, being mounted. Bradley had promised to ship them back to Spindrift by sea.

Canton Charlie made his way through the empty tables, followed by a Chinese who carried a tray laden with glasses.

"More dragon's blood, meaning coke," Zircon said with a smile. "I suggest we drink a toast to success and then get down to business. Carl, you've kept us waiting long enough to hear your story."

"It's the sort of tale that should be heard on a full stomach," the ethnologist said. "That's why I've made you wait. Now that we've filled up on Charlie's excellent chow, we'll talk. We have a little while before the mob gathers."

Bradley had insisted that all of them, including Keaton-Yeats, dine with him at the Golden Mouse before swapping experiences and completing the story of the heavy water. They had eaten real Cantonese food, each using chopsticks, and they were full to the ears.

Scotty grinned at Canton Charlie. "We owe you an apology," he said.

The proprietor of the Golden Mouse shook his head. "The other way around. Carl and Chahda told me you would come. If I'd kept a better lookout while waiting for Carl to come after I sent him a message, that Portuguese would never have had a chance to tip off Long Shadow, and the Chinese who dropped the message would have been caught in the act."

After talking it over, they had decided that the Por-

tuguese seaman who had been giving himself a manicure with a dagger probably had been the one who
tipped off Long Shadow about three Americans who
had asked for Chahda. Of course Long Shadow knew
of Chahda's connection with Bradley because of the in-
cidents in Singapore.

Canton Charlie grinned evilly. "That Portuguese
won't do any more spyin' for Long Shadow."

His meaning was clear. Rick's eyes met Scotty's.

"Pull up a chair, Charlie," Carl Bradley said. "We'll
drink a toast in coke to our former pals. Long Shadow
and Worthington Ko."

Zircon lifted his glass, then took a sip. "Long Shadow
said he and Ko were finished," he recalled. "And you
said as much in your note, or implied it. But I'm hanged
if I know why they're finished. They were healthy
enough when we left them at Korse Lenken."

Bradley smiled without mirth. "To understand their
punishment, you must understand what has happened.
Suppose I start at the beginning?"

"Best place," Chahda said. "Better start at Singapore,
boss. Plenty I don't know, too."

"All right, Chahda. To begin with, I first heard about
heavy water in Singapore from an informant with
whom I deal. I'm no physicist, of course. I wouldn't
know heavy water if I were served coffee made with
the stuff. But I saw the implications right away and I
sent a cable to Washington. You know about that because Steve Ames contacted Hartson Brant, if I'm
right."

"You're right," Rick agreed.

"At the time I knew nothing except that heavy water had appeared in Singapore. I continued investigations at top speed. I managed to locate the house which was headquarters for the heavy-water dealers, again with the aid of an informant. At first I thought the stuff was coming overland, down the Malay Peninsula. Then I learned it was being shipped in by boat from Hong Kong."

Customers were starting to come into the Golden Mouse. Bradley lowered his voice so as not to be overheard. "At the same time, the dealers spotted Chahda and me. It wasn't hard to do for an expert such as we were up against. I walked into our hotel room and was jumped by Worthington Ko and some Chinese thugs. We had it hot and heavy for a while and some blood was shed." He grinned. "Not mine, I'm happy to say. I managed to get clear and decided I'd better drop out of sight. So I became a Eurasian seaman. It's a disguise I've used before, and it's quite safe.

Rick studied Bradley's face. He had a bone-deep tan, and his face, although pleasant, had no really distinguishing features. It was easy to see how he could become a Eurasian. Disguise, after all, was just putting yourself into a part. It wasn't a matter of make-up.

"I hurried to Hong Kong," Bradley went on, "sure that Chahda would piece together the story enough to follow me. I stopped at Saigon on the way and contacted our legation there. The minister had received the cable sent to all missions in the Far East giving your names, descriptions, and time of arrival in Hong Kong."

"The timing must have been close," Scotty said.

"It was. The legation had received the cable only hours before my arrival. It probably was the day you left New York."

"Also I think it was day I left Singapore," Chahda said.

"I got to Hong Kong and contacted Charlie," Bradley continued. "Tell us what you found out, Charlie."

Charlie shrugged. "No trouble. I got in touch with a pal in the Chinese Beggar's Guild. He checked up and found out that a lot of coolies carrying goatskin water bags were crossing from China to Kowloon and from Kowloon to the island. Of course a lot of that goes on, anyway. But some of the coolies weren't selling their water. I got my hands on one of the coolies and we sort of told him he ought to sing us a song about where the water came from." Charlie grinned. "He sang all right. He yodeled real good, about Korse Lenken. He also said Long Shadow had been at the monastery."

"Do you know Long Shadow?" Rick asked Bradley.

"Yes. I'd never met him, but I knew him by reputation."

Charlie stood up. "Got to take care of the customers. See you later."

As he left, Bradley continued, "Next step was to get a line on the source of the heavy water. We had the name of Korse Lenken, but that was all. I assumed it was being produced industrially somewhere on the Tibetan border. But that would take equipment, of course,

so I put the consulate commercial section to work finding out if Long Shadow had been dabbling in industrial
equipment. That's routine for a consulate. Well, he
hadn't. But what turned up but the fact that he had im-
ported some Nansen bottles."

"I begin to see how it shaped up," Zircon said.

"It wasn't difficult, really," Bradley admitted. "Just
took plugging. At that time, Chahda arrived from Singapore, bringing Long Shadow with him, although he
didn't know it."

"Unhappy me," Chahda complained.

Bradley smiled at the Hindu boy. "Don't be unhappy.
Long Shadow is the best in the business. Well, I told
Chahda to go to Korse Lenken, then dropped my disguise. As I had hoped, Long Shadow started following
me, dropping Chahda. Once Chahda was on his way,
I ditched Long Shadow and became the Eurasian once
more. We had given Charlie instructions about you.
He got in touch with me the moment you showed up,
but I was delayed. Meanwhile, you had been spotted,
probably when you asked for Chahda. Long Shadow
must have figured the odds were piling up. He'd lost
me, so he probably decided to keep the odds down by
removing all of you."

He nodded at Keaton-Yeats. "Thanks to our young
British friend, we found you before you'd been knocked
in the head. Then I took off after Long Shadow, as you
know. Somewhere between times I'd gotten the consul
to get a Nansen bottle, a rubber boat, and that other
stuff for you. I didn't know why you'd need the rubber

boat, but I figured a Nansen bottle meant water and you'd better be prepared."

"If we hadn't been trapped in the caverns, we could have used the rubber boat," Rick said. "But it was at camp with Sing when we needed it."

"Fortunes of war," Bradley said. "Well, while you were sneaking around through the caves, I kept busy. You probably know that the Far East is the happiest spying ground in the world. There are so many spies they have to spy on each other." He turned suddenly to Keaton-Yeats. "Isn't that right, colleague?"

The young Englishman's expression never changed. "And some are almighty good," he said calmly. "Like Bradley. Soon as I knew he was on the case, I reported to my superiors and we dropped the thing like a hot potato, just to avoid being at cross-purposes. We knew that the Americans would tip us off as soon as they had a definite answer."

The boys stared at Keaton-Yeats. "But you're a bank clerk!" Rick exclaimed.

"He's also a British intelligence agent," Bradley said, grinning. "That's why I insisted he come tonight. We've already informed the British, through channels, that the heavy-water menace no longer exists. Keaton-Yeats is here tonight to get the details."

"You chaps would be simply amazed at how much valuable information one picks up in a bank," Keaton-Yeats said. "Astounding. Although I must say having lads ask for golden mice is a bit unusual."

Scotty shook his head. "And you looked so innocent,"

he complained. "We believed everything you said."

The young Englishman grinned. "I am innocent," he replied. "No woolly little lamb could be more so. And I did tell you the blessed truth, you know, even though I didn't mention I had a bit of a job to do as well as having an interest in your welfare. Our own chaps had discovered heavy water was coming into Hong Kong, too, so naturally we were interested. But since Bradley was already on the job, and we co-operate with you Americans on matters atomic, we sat back and waited."

"I'm astonished," Zircon admitted. "But get on with your story, Carl."

"Right. As I said, spies spy on each other. I contacted a French agent I know, and in the course of having lunch with him I casually asked how much he had paid for the information about an atomic pile. I was just fishing, of course. Well, he took the bait. He leaped at it like a striking tuna. I knew I had something then. From there on, it wasn't hard to uncover the whole business, just by making contact with the espionage agents of various countries."

The JANIG man wet his throat with another sip of coke. "And business is just what it was. I can't say how long ago Long Shadow found out there was heavy water in the Caves of Fear. I did find out that in his younger days he was something of a scientist and that he explored the Korse Lenken region thoroughly. That was shortly before the discovery of heavy water in Lake Baikal. I think we can assume that he pieced the story together and realized that the lake in the caverns had the same possibilities. It would have been only a matter of scientific curiosity then, but with recent developments in the atomic field, the possibilities took on a new light."

He paused as a Filipino brushed by, then resumed, lowering his voice so only those at the table could hear. "He's a smart one. I've known about him for a long time, as one of the best free-lance agents in the Far East. He has a good reputation for accuracy, and he sells—or sold—information to the highest bidder. He was riding on his reputation in this deal, because as soon as the facts became known, as they had to sooner or later, he was all washed up as a spy."

"I don't get it," Rick complained.

"I'll explain. He was selling a story to every country that was interested. He would contact the embassy, consulate, or chief espionage agent of, say, country X. He would report that country Y had a secret atomic pile—nuclear reactor, that is—in the mountains of West China. You can imagine the excitement. He would sell that information for a reasonable price. Then, for a considerably higher price, he would undertake to collect a sample of the deuterium they were using. Once he collected the sample, which of course came from Korse Lenken, he would contract to give them the location of the reactor for a very high price indeed. He made the rounds country by country, changing his story as needed. Of course he collected in advance for the location, which was to be delivered later, after he had risked his life getting it. That was the story he used—and some of the best agents in the Orient fell for it."

The daring ingenuity of the thing made Rick shake his head. "But they were certain to catch up with him!"

"Of course. He knew it. But he intended to stall in giving them the final location until he had tapped every possible source. Then I believe he intended handing them some phony location in West China, after which he would disappear and live on the proceeds. He collected enough to make him very wealthy. He hadn't reached us yet, but you can bet that if I hadn't stumbled on the story, he would have made a sale to one of our embassies or consulates."

"Ours, too," Keaton-Yeats said. "He took advantage of all the interest in atomic weapons. And of his reputation, of course."

"What about Ko?" Scotty asked.

"Ko had a side line," Bradley explained. "He was selling heavy water to various institutions and schools all over Asia for normal experimental purposes. He claimed to be importing it from England. That was why they were bringing so much out."

"That is also how we got interested," Keaton-Yeats said. "We got queries about more heavy water at a lower price from one of the schools that had bought Ko's product. Naturally, we knew no heavy water was coming from England, so we got interested very quickly."

"We sure dropped a monkey wrench in a gold mine," Rick said.

"Evidently," Zircon agreed. "But you haven't explained why Long Shadow and Ko are finished."

Keaton-Yeats laughed grimly.

Bradley stretched his legs out. "Easy. The story had already spread about heavy water at Korse Lenken. Ronnie and I got the good word circulating right after we received your cable from Chungking. By now all the countries he sold his story to—and that is most countries—know they've been done in the eye, as our British friend would say. Do you know the penalty for a double cross in the espionage racket?"

"A bullet, a knife, or a blunt instrument," Keaton-Yeats said. "It's as certain as tomorrow's dawn."

Bradley nodded. "Also, the lamas won't permit the two of them to remain after their wounds are healed. They are evil men, and the lamas know it. Sooner or later, they'll have to leave the mountains and enter civilization. I know their type. They might survive if they wanted to live alone in the mountains like two wolves. But they won't."

Rick shuddered. He knew from experience what it was like to be hunted. Ko and Long Shadow would be hunted by agents of a dozen countries or more once they set foot in civilization. After that, it was only a matter of time. The two couldn't escape for long.

"Now," Bradley said, "let's have the details of your trip."

A burly English seaman brushed past.

"I'll be quick," Zircon said. "You know . . ."

Bradley let out a yelp as the seaman stepped squarely

on his foot. "Watch out where you're going, you big ox!" he exclaimed.

The seaman stopped short. "Who you callin' a ruddy ox, you little blighter?" He grabbed Bradley by the collar.

The JANIG man's hands moved in a blur of speed. One struck the seaman's hand away. The second caught him just above the solar plexus. The seaman rocked backward, stumbled over a table occupied by three Portuguese, and crashed to the floor, taking the table with him. One Portuguese clubbed the seaman over the head with a bottle. The second threw a glass at Bradley. The third picked up a chair.

"Look out!" Scotty yelled. He flung his coke into the face of the chair wielder, then jumped to grab the chair. The Portuguese, who had swung the bottle, threw it at Scotty, missed, and knocked the glass out of the hand of a Sikh seated at a near-by table. The Sikh rose with a battle yell and leaped.

Rick lost track after that. For a moment he stood amazed, then jumped to help Chahda, who was being tackled from behind by one of the Portuguese. Canton Charlie's was in an uproar. The fight had spread like fire in dead leaves. Rick hadn't been aware of the place filling up, but it was definitely full. Bottles and glasses flew.

He ducked a wild swing with a chair, then as he stood up he brought the table with him, dumping it over on three Chinese who were struggling with Scotty. A fist caught him behind the ear. He kicked backward, then whirled, his elbow catching a Filipino sailor in the chest. The Filipino sprawled backward.

A bottle whizzed past Rick's ear. He ducked, then rushed to Zircon. The big scientist was holding a British seaman in each hand, busily knocking their heads together. Scotty rose out of his path, swinging. A Eurasian who had been about to swing with a bottle stopped short, swaying, as Scotty's fist connected. The bottle dropped on Chahda, who was crawling out from under a table.

An American sailor rushed past, one arm catching Rick and sending him sprawling. Rick swung wildly, and pulled his punch just in time to keep from bashing Keaton-Yeats, who was busy with a swarthy man with gold rings in his ears. The place was a madhouse. Bradley went headlong at Rick's feet, jumped up again like a rubber ball, and plunged into the fray. Rick saw with amazement that he was grinning from ear to ear.

A Portuguese rose from nowhere and aimed a roundhouse swing at Rick's head. He ducked, then put all his weight into an overhand chop, missed, and fell against the Portuguese. The man threw him off and caught him behind the ear with a short hook. Rick shook his head, dazed. Another punch caught him on the cheek. He lost his temper then and flailed out. One fist connected solidly. The Portuguese vanished, to be replaced by someone else. Rick swung until his arms were leaden. Then, in the midst of the turmoil, came a stentorian bellow.

"Here! Listen!"

He turned. Canton Charlie was standing on the bar, and a sawed-off shotgun roamed impartially over the crowd. "The first man who pulls a knife gets this!" he shouted.

There was a roar from the mob, and the instant of silence dissolved into a melee again. Rick turned back to see how his friends were doing and saw a fist coming at him. He tried to bring his hands up, but he was too slow. The fist got bigger and bigger and bigger and exploded into bright lights. His knees buckled. He drifted off into peace and quiet.

CHAPTER XX

Home Flight

"THE GOLDEN MOUSE," Keaton-Yeats said judiciously, "is rapidly becoming a purple mouse." He tilted Rick's face to the light. "I also see other colors. By the time you get home, a rainbow will be rather pale and dull by comparison."

"I got a mouse hung on me all right," Rick said. "And I didn't even see who did it."

"I did," Scotty volunteered. "It was a British seaman. Chahda polished him off with a bottle before you even hit the floor."

Zircon wrapped gauze around Bradley's knuckles. "For an ethnologist, which is a peaceful profession, you are mighty quick to take offense," he stated.

"My boss is a sudden man," Chahda said from the bed where he lay with a wet cloth on his head.

They were in their room at the Peninsular Hotel. Rick had recovered under the urging of a bucket of water in the hands of Canton Charlie. He was still wet. He stripped off his shirt and grinned as he looked around him. All of them bore souvenirs. His own probably was the most colorful, consisting of a black eye that covered nearly half of his face. Scotty had a welt across his forehead that would last several days. Bradley had lost most of the skin off the knuckles of his right hand. Zircon moved gingerly, favoring his bruised ribs. Chahda and Keaton-Yeats bore painful egg-shaped lumps from swung bottles.

"Happens at Charlie's every night," Bradley said. "Can't disappoint the customers. Only a question of who starts it. Tonight I happened to be the one. You get so you rather enjoy it after a while."

"As a sport, it will never replace checkers," Scotty said. He winced as his fingers explored the welt on his forehead.

Rick chuckled. He could see what Bradley meant. As long as Canton Charlie's shotgun ensured fair play, to the extent of no knives, it was just a free-for-all such as might happen anywhere—at least where seamen gathered.

"It's like swimming in cold water," he said. "Getting in is tough, but it's kind of fun once you've made the plunge."

Bradley flexed his bandaged hand. "That's right. Now, it's getting late and I still want to hear about your experiences. Hobart, want to pick up where we left off?"

They found seats on the beds and in the wicker chairs

while the big scientist told of their adventures in Korse Lenken, with assists from the boys. When he had finished, Keaton-Yeats sighed. "I wish now I'd gone with you," he said. "Nothing dull where you Americans go. While you were barging around caves, I was making change at the bank. Very dull."

"I guess that ties up all the loose ends," Bradley said. "And it makes quite a package."

"Even without a nuclear reactor or any potential atom bombs," Rick added. "Anyway, we couldn't know until we investigated that there wasn't some kind of atomic menace in the offing."

"Right," Zircon agreed. "I must say, however, that I have a fine story for one of the scientific journals. My analysis of the water samples shows a layer almost a foot deep of nearly pure deuterium. It's an amazing phenomenon which will require more of a theory than just the heavy water settling. Settling wouldn't produce a fraction of the amount. I'm taking the samples home for further analysis, along with some samples of limestone from the caves. Who knows? This may produce a scientific finding of some significance."

"It may," Bradley agreed. "I hope it does, because then the trip will have made some contribution to the sum total of our knowledge besides contributing information to the JANIG files."

"And the files of our office," Keaton-Yeats added.

Rick looked at Chahda. "What now for you? Going to stay in the Far East for a while?"

The Hindu boy smiled. "Not so very long. I think now

I go back to Bombay, see my family for a while, then I will come to Spindrift."

"Swell!" Scotty exclaimed. "We've missed you, half pint."

Zircon and Rick echoed the sentiment.

"No point in our staying on," the scientist said. "If we can get space, we'll take off on tomorrow's flight." He smiled. "It will be good to get back to our peaceful lab, eh, lads?"

"Yes," Scotty agreed.

"Definitely," Rick said.

And even as they spoke, halfway across the world hammer strokes completed a structure that would mean anything but peace, a story to be told in the next volume:

STAIRWAY TO DANGER